WILLIAM K. DURR • **JEAN M. LE PERE** • **RUTH BROWN**

CONSULTANT • **PAUL McKEE**

LINGUISTIC ADVISOR • **JACK E. KITTELL**

PANORAMA

HOUGHTON MIFFLIN COMPANY • BOSTON

NEW YORK • ATLANTA • GENEVA, ILLINOIS • DALLAS • PALO ALTO

Acknowledgments

For each of the selections listed below, grateful acknowledgment is made for permission to adapt and/or reprint copyrighted material, as follows:

"The Answers," from *Forever X* by Robert Clairmont, copyright 1951 by Robert Clairmont. Published with the permission of Contemporary Poetry.

The Braille Alphabet. Our thanks to Field Enterprises Educational Corporation, publishers of the *World Book* Encyclopedia, for permission to use their helpful picture and information.

"Eddie and the Doll." From *Eddie and His Big Deals* by Carolyn Haywood. Reprinted by permission of William Morrow and Company, Inc. Copyright © 1955 by Carolyn Haywood.

"Elephant Wood." Reprinted by permission of David McKay Company, Inc., from *Magic Wherever You Are* by Bill Severn. Copyright © 1957 by Bill Severn. British rights granted by Faber and Faber, Ltd.

"Falling Leaves," by M. Caporale Shecktor and Harriet May Savitz. From *Ranger Rick's Nature Magazine,* published by the National Wildlife Federation.

"Feet," by Aileen Fisher. "Feet" is reprinted with the permission of Charles Scribner's Sons from *Cricket in a Thicket* by Aileen Fisher. Copyright © 1961 by Aileen Fisher.

"Foal," from *Menagerie* by Mary Britton Miller. Reprinted with permission of the author.

"The Friendly Ghost," by Elizabeth Yates. Reprinted by permission of the author.

"Golden Boy," by Willis Lindquist. Adapted by permission of the author from "Golden Boy," *Story Parade,* May, 1954.

"High, Wide, and Handsome." Adapted from *High, Wide, and Handsome* by Jean Merrill. Copyright 1964 by Jean Merrill. Permission granted by the Publisher, William R. Scott, Inc.

"How D. Y. B. Worked for April." From *Bright April,* by Marguerite de Angeli. Copyright © 1946 by Marguerite de Angeli. Reprinted by permission of Doubleday & Company, Inc.

"The Hut," by Hilda Van Stockum. Reprinted with the permission of the author and The Horn Book, Inc., publishers.

"Let Me Tell You About Arthur . . ." by Bernard Waber. "Let Me Tell You About Arthur . . ." from *An Anteater Named Arthur,* © 1967 by Bernard Waber. Permission granted by the publisher, Houghton Mifflin Company.

"Magic in a Glass Jar." Adapted by permission of Coward-McCann, Inc., from "Magic in a Glass Jar" from *The People Downstairs and Other City Stories* by Rhoda Bacmeister. Copyright © 1964 by Rhoda Bacmeister.

"McBroom Tells the Truth." Reprinted from *McBroom Tells the Truth* by Sid Fleischman.

Contents

ORBITS

SPHERES

REALMS

ORBITS

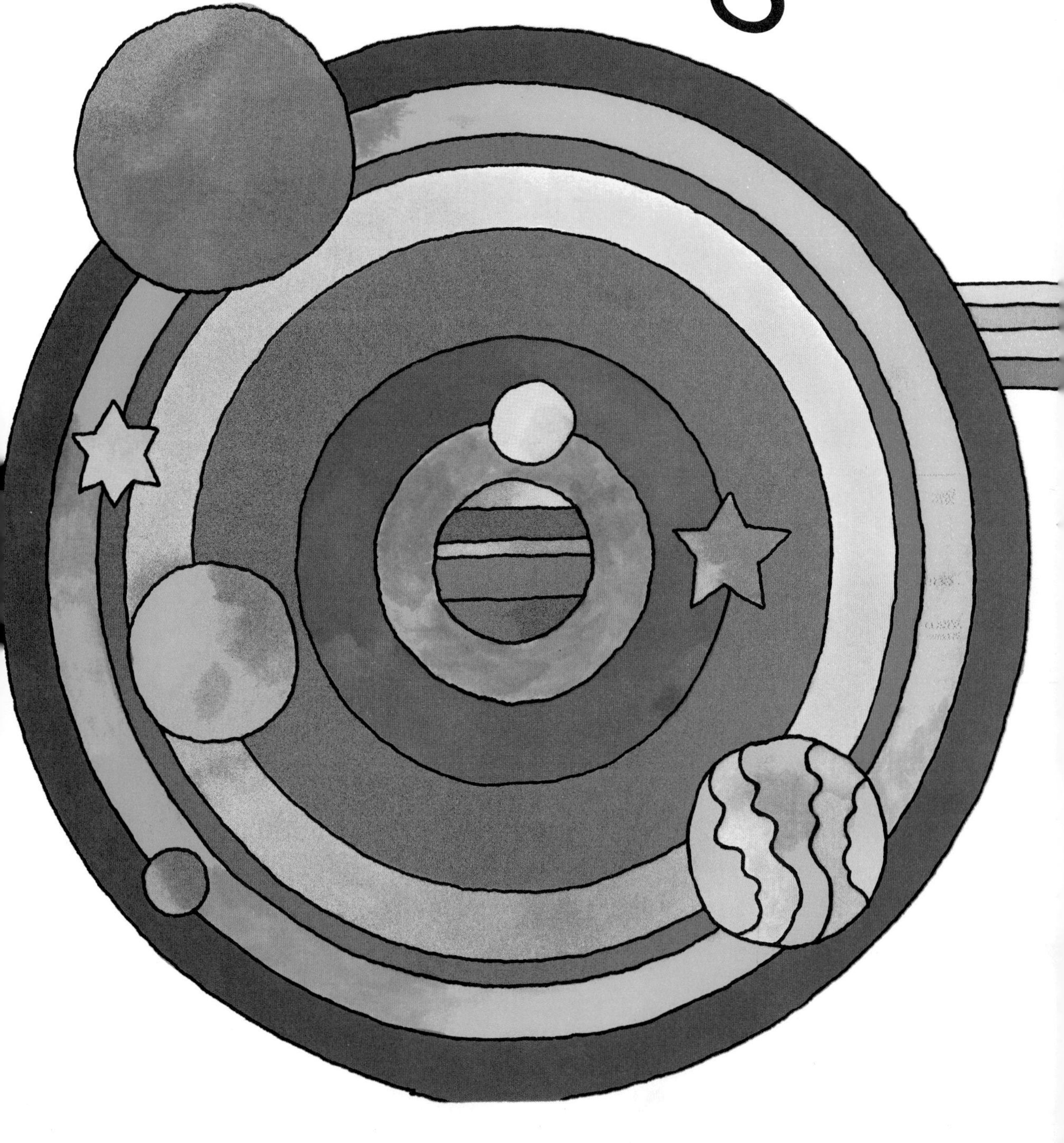

ORBITS

The Snake in the Carpool

by Miriam Schlein

One Sunday, while walking through the high weeds, Betsy found a snake. It was gray with a yellow neck, and yellow underneath. Betsy liked all sorts of wild things, but she had never had a snake before because:

1. Her mother hated snakes.

2. Her father did not care for them, either.

3. Her little brother would try to pinch it, bite it, or hide it if she took it into the house.

4. She had found a snake once before, and her mother had said: "NO SNAKES IN THE HOUSE!"

But her mother had not said, "NO SNAKES *OUT* OF THE HOUSE." So Betsy caught the snake. She put it into a little jar. It was a little snake. Then she quickly went inside and got a small basket and put a lot of grass into it. She put the snake into the basket, closed the top, and left it outside.

The next morning was Monday. Betsy got dressed quickly. She had to be ready for the carpool.

This is not the kind of pool that you swim in. It was just that when she went to school each morning, she went in a car with three other children: Mark, Jill, and Ronnie. One day one mother drove them. Then another day another mother drove them. This is called a carpool.

All the children sometimes took little things with them to school to show their friends: a book, a doll, a seashell. So Betsy said to herself, "I'll take the snake."

When Mark's mother came to pick her up, Betsy took the basket with the snake. She got into the back seat with Mark, Jill, and Ronnie. She put the basket on the floor alongside of some boxes.

"What's in the basket, Betsy?" asked Mark.

"It's a secret," said Betsy. "I'll show you in school."

She wondered to herself if the teacher, too, would say, "NO SNAKES!" But she would have to take a chance now.

"Is it something to eat?" asked Ronnie.

"Oh, no."

"Oh, come on, show us," said Jill.

"You won't be afraid?" asked Betsy.

"Afraid?" said Ronnie. His eyes got wide. "What is it?"

"All right," said Betsy. "I'll show you."

She put the basket on her lap and opened the top a crack. "It's buried in the grass," she whispered.

She opened the top wide and felt in the grass with her fingers. "It's gone!" said Betsy.

"What was it?" asked Mark.

"A snake."

"A snake!" said Mark.

"Will it bite?" asked Jill.

"Oh, my little snake! Where is it?" said Betsy.

"Look," said Ronnie. "Here's how it got out." He poked his finger into the basket. "There's a hole in the basket."

"Let's find it," said Mark.

They stuck their hands down in the edges of the seat. Mark got down to look on the floor.

"It's not any place!" he whispered.

"It has to be," whispered Betsy.

Usually when they went to school in the car, the mother driving would say, every once in a while, "Quiet down, now!" as the children yelled or pushed or poked each other. But now they were so quiet that Mark's mother turned around to look at them. They were *too* quiet.

"What's wrong, children?" she asked.

"Oh, nothing, Mom," said Mark.

Ronnie picked up the two boxes that were on the floor. He shook them. "What's in these?"

"Oh, just some things my mother has to return to the store," said Mark.

"Here we are, children," said Mark's mother.

"He probably wiggled out the window," said Ronnie.

"Or out the door," said Jill.

"But how?" said Betsy. "Oh, dear."

She brushed the grass from the basket out of the car door.

"What's all that, Betsy?" asked Mark's mother.

"Grass," said Betsy.

She cleaned it all out of the car, then took her empty basket, and went to school.

Mark's mother turned the car around.

"I will just have time," she thought, "to return these things to Hillingdale's."

She turned around to the back seat to make sure her packages were there. "There's that dress I decided I just don't like. And those pajamas I bought for Mark were too big."

Now how could she know that curled up in the pocket of the too-big pajamas was a little gray snake with a yellow neck?

First she returned her dress. Then she went to the pajama counter and said to the saleslady, "I would like to exchange these pajamas, please. They are too large for my boy. I think we need a size 8."

The saleslady said, "Oh, yes, here is an 8." Then she turned to a woman who was standing nearby, and she said, "I'm sorry, but we don't have a size 10 in the drip-dry, short-sleeved pajamas."

The woman said, "Oh, dear," and turned away.

"Wait," said Mark's mother. "I'm returning a size 10. Maybe you would like these."

"Well, thank you," said the other woman. "Red and white stripes! They feel nice and soft. But red and white stripes! Would he like red? It's for my nephew, you see. It's his birthday."

"Boys like stripes," said the saleslady.

"I'll take this pair!" said the woman. "You can leave them right in that box."

Now how could *she* know that curled up in the pocket of the birthday pajamas lay a little gray snake with a yellow neck?

"I Don't Believe It!"

"Happy birthday, Homer dear," the woman who had taken the pajamas said to her nephew as she handed him the box. Then she left him to play with his friends, Barney and Paul. She went into the kitchen to talk to his mother.

As Homer opened the box, out crawled the little snake.

"A snake!" said Barney.

"It's just what I wanted, Aunt Gladys!" shouted Homer to his aunt.

"Your Aunt Gladys is a good sport," said Paul. "My aunt wouldn't give *me* a snake."

"Do you like the color, dear?" called his aunt.

"It's a beauty," said Homer, holding the little snake on his finger.

"Is the size all right?" she asked.

"It's just perfect," said Homer.

"Let me hold him," said Barney.

"All right," said Homer. He ran into the kitchen. "It's the greatest birthday present I ever got!" he said to his aunt.

"I'm glad, dear," she said, just a little surprised. "Well, I have to leave now. Good-by," and she went off.

"Mother," said Homer. "Can I have some sugar, or raisins, or something?"

"What for?" asked his mother.

"To feed him," said Homer.

"Feed what?"

"My snake," said Homer. "The snake that Aunt Gladys gave me."

"Aunt Gladys gave you a snake? I don't believe it!"

"Hey, Homer," called Paul from the next room. "He went under the couch. We can't get him."

Homer's mother ran inside, bent down, and looked under the couch.

"Oh, my goodness!" she said.

Just then Homer's father came home.

"Martin," said Homer's mother. "Your sister Gladys gave Homer a snake for his birthday!"

"A snake!" said his father. "Gladys?"

He looked under the couch. Then he turned to Homer. "Son, are you telling the truth? Did you get that from Aunt Gladys?"

"Honest, Dad," said Homer. "It came in that box. From Hillingdale's."

"Then we can just return it," said Homer's mother.

"But, Mom," said Homer. "He's so nice. I want to keep him."

"It must be a mistake in packing," said his father. He ran into the bedroom and came back with a pair of gloves. "I'll catch it," he said, "but it might be dangerous. When I count three," he said to the boys, "pick up the couch. One. Two. Three."

They picked up the couch.

He grabbed the snake and dropped it into a jar.

"Where are you going?" asked Homer's mother.

"I'm going to show it to Bill Wentworth. He lives down the street. He works at the museum, and he'll know if it's a harmful snake."

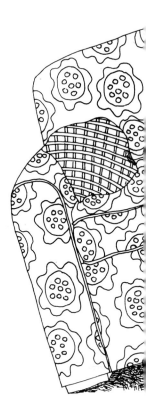

"Can I keep him, Mom?" asked Homer. "He's so small. I'll keep him in a cage. A snake cage."

"We'll see, dear," said his mother. "I don't know. Well, look at these lovely pajamas."

"They're pretty nice," said Homer. "But I still want the snake!"

The door slammed. Homer's father came back. He had taken his gloves off. "It's a ringneck snake," he said. "Perfectly harmless. We'll keep it tonight. Tomorrow morning we'll let it out in the woods."

"But Dad, it was a present!" said Homer. "And Mom said maybe I could keep him. In a snake cage."

His father looked at his mother.

"It's all right with me if it's harmless," she said. "But Homer will have to feed it and take care of it himself."

"I will," said Homer.

"I'm sure it was a mistake of some sort," said his father, "but HAPPY BIRTHDAY, HOMER."

And he gave Homer back his snake.

Home Sweet Home

Meanwhile, back at the carpool, Mark's mother had picked up Betsy, Mark, Ronnie, and Jill after school.

"Did you find anything in the car, Mrs. Nichols?" asked Betsy.

"No, Betsy, why? Did you leave your sweater?"

"No," said Betsy.

"Maybe it went into one of those boxes," whispered Ronnie.

"Mom, what's in these boxes?" asked Mark.

"Some things from Hillingdale's," said his mother. "I just bought them."

"But the boxes were here before," said Ronnie.

"No, they were other boxes," said Mark's mother. "I returned those to Hillingdale's. These are different ones."

"Hillingdale's!" said Betsy.

"That's where he must be," whispered Ronnie.

"What will he do in Hillingdale's?" sighed Betsy. "That's no place for a snake."

Homer kept his birthday snake in the garage. Early the next morning he went out and dropped some little pieces of toast and raisins into the jar.

"Hi there, little ringneck snake." Homer

rapped his finger against the jar. "Hey, I think
I'll call you Ringer!"

"Homer! Homer Winthrop!"

He heard his mother calling.

"OK, Mom."

He went in and got ready for school.

At school, Homer sat next to Barney.

"How's the snake?" whispered Barney.

"OK," whispered Homer.

"Quiet back there," said the teacher.

"What did you feed him?" whispered Barney.

Homer wrote something in his notebook.
Then he gave Barney a poke.

Barney leaned over. Homer had written in
the notebook: "Raisins and Toast."

"Name two things that the farmers grow in Ohio," said the teacher. "Barney Ferguson."

Barney looked up.

"Raisins and toast," he said.

The class giggled.

"That's not funny," said the teacher.

"I mean corn," said Barney. "They grow wheat and corn."

"That's better," said the teacher.

After school, Barney said, "You nearly got me into trouble."

"I did not," said Homer. "You asked me. Anyhow, are you coming over this afternoon?"

"Sure," said Barney.

"Bring a hammer," said Homer.

"What for?" asked Paul.

"I've got to start building the snake cage," said Homer. "Do you want to help me?"

"Of course," said Barney.

"Me, too," said Paul.

They were over in five minutes with hammers. They peeked in at the snake.

"He's still sleeping," said Barney.

"He doesn't look healthy to me," said Paul.

"I think you're making him sick on that food you gave him," said Barney.

"I don't think he ate any," said Homer, with his eye against the jar.

"That's what I mean," said Barney. "Don't they eat lizards or something?"

"Look," said Paul. "Why don't we go to the library and find out?"

"Find out what?" asked Homer.

"Find out what snakes like to eat," said Paul. "We'll get a snake book."

"Good idea," said Homer. "Come on."

The librarian found them a book called *Snakes, Large and Small.* It had a curled-up snake on the cover.

Homer sat right down on the floor and flipped through the pages.

"Snakes," said Homer, reading aloud, "eat worms, salamanders, lizards . . ."

"See," said Barney. "No raisins. No toast."

"We'll take this one," Homer said to the librarian.

Now they knew what real snake food was.

Every day, after school, they would look for snake food. Down by the river and under rocks, they looked for tiny lizards and salamanders. Behind the garage, they dug for worms.

It took them the rest of the week to build the

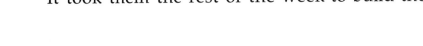

snake cage. It was a big wooden box, with glass on one side. It had airholes on top. And on one end there was a little door.

They dropped Ringer in.

"Home sweet home," said Homer. And he shut the door.

Ringer or Snaky?

The next morning, Homer decided to take Ringer for a walk. He dropped him back into the jar.

There was a bunch of girls down the street playing around. "I'll show it to them," thought Homer. "I bet they'll scream."

He went up to a little girl in a striped dress. "Look what I've got," he said. "Boo!" He stuck the jar in front of her nose.

But instead of screaming, the little girl just grinned. "My goodness," she said. "Where did you find him?" And she took the jar.

Homer was so surprised, he just let her take it.

She opened the jar, took Ringer out, and held him right in her hand.

"Hey, what are you doing?" said Homer. "He'll get away."

"Don't call me 'hey.' It's my snake," said the little girl, whose name was Betsy.

"What do you mean, *your* snake?" Homer yelled. "He's mine. I got him for my birthday!"

He made a grab for the snake.

"Quiet!" said the little girl. "You'll scare him."

"Just give him to me," said Homer. "He's mine. My Aunt Gladys bought him for me in

Hillingdale's. He was gift-wrapped, and every-thing!"

"Hillingdale's!" said Betsy. "That proves he's mine. I caught him and took him to school. But he escaped from me and went into a Hilling-dale's box. See? I bet your Aunt Gladys didn't even *know* he was in the box."

She looked down at the snake. "I'm sure glad you found him, anyway," she said. "Thanks." She began to walk away.

Homer tried to make another grab for Ringer, but there seemed to be seven or eight little girls that kept getting in his way.

"What *is* this?" he yelled. "Give me my snake."

Betsy stopped and turned around. "If you're so sure he's your snake, go ask your Aunt Gladys."

"All right," said Homer. "I will. I'll call her right now."

He marched into the house with Betsy trailing after him. He phoned his aunt.

"Hello," he said. "Aunt Gladys. I want to ask you about the present you gave me."

"Hello, dear," said Aunt Gladys. "Do they fit?"

"Fit?" said Homer. "What fit?"

"The pajamas," said Aunt Gladys.

"Not the pajamas," said Homer. "The snake."

"SNAKE! What snake?"

"The snake you gave me," said Homer.

Betsy stuck her ear next to the phone.

"Homer," she heard the voice say. "I know

this is a joke. I never gave you a snake. I gave you pajamas. Red and white pajamas."

"Oh," said Homer. "OK, Aunt Gladys. Good-by now." He hung up sadly.

"Well," said Homer. "I guess you're right. I guess he's yours after all. Although it sounds kind of crazy to me. If he went in the box, why didn't you get him out?"

"Because I didn't know he was *in* it," said Betsy, "till the box got returned to the store."

Betsy just stood around. She looked down and saw the snake cage.

"What's that?" she asked. "Is it his?"

"Of course it's his." Homer gave the cage an angry little kick. Then he was sorry he did it. "It sure took us a long time to build that thing," he mumbled.

"Mmmm," said Betsy. "I guess so. It's nice."

She walked a few steps, then turned around. "Well," she said. "If I need any advice about Snaky, I'll come and ask you."

"His name," said Homer stiffly, "is Ringer."

Betsy giggled. "Ringer. That's a silly name for a snake."

"It's not silly. He's a ringneck snake. So there. And if you want some advice, he eats worms and very small lizards and salamanders."

"Salamanders," said Betsy. "Well, for goodness sake. What's that, and where do I get them?"

"I can show you," said Homer. "You get them down by the river . . . and . . ." He stared down at the cage with its grass and rocks and the clamshell filled with water. What was he going to do with the old cage, anyhow?

Homer looked up from the cage back to the little girl.

"Hey," he said slowly. "What's your name?"

"Betsy."

"Mine's Homer. Look. I've got an idea. You found Snaky, I mean Ringer — but I kept him nice and safe, and gave him a home. I know what he likes to eat, and everything. Why don't we be partners?"

"Partners?"

"Yes. Partners! He can be half mine and half yours. He can live here, because I've got the cage — but you can come and see him, and play with him, and feed him any old time. Even when I'm not here! How about that? Hmmm? Come on. Think about it!"

"I'm thinking," said Betsy. If she took her snake home, she could just see her mother standing there at the door, saying, "GET THAT THING OUT OF HERE. INSTANTLY!"

"I think it's a good idea — but . . ."

"But what?" said Homer.

"Well," said Betsy. "Can I bring my friends around to see him? My friends from the car-pool?"

"Sure," said Homer. "Any time. Then we're partners?"

"Partners!" said Betsy.

Just then Barney and Paul came along.

"Who's this?" asked Barney.

"And what's she doing with Ringer?" asked Paul.

"She's my partner," said Homer. And he told them the story.

"Snake partners. Hey, that's funny," said Paul. "Wait a minute. Why shouldn't we be partners, too?" He looked at Barney.

"We helped build the cage," Barney reminded Homer.

"We looked for food," said Paul.

Betsy looked at Homer. "It's fine with me," she said.

"OK," said Homer. "Now give me back my . . . I mean, I think he ought to go back in the cage. Come on, Ringer."

"I'll put him in," Betsy said. She gently dropped the snake into the cage.

"She handles him very well," whispered Paul.

"Well, she caught him with her bare hands," said Homer.

"Do you really believe that?" whispered Paul.

"Sure," said Homer. "I can tell."

Betsy stood up. "Hey," she said. "We forgot to shake."

"Shake what?" asked Barney.

"Shake hands!" said Betsy. "Because we're partners."

"Shake," said Homer.

They all shook hands.

"I have to go home now," said Betsy. "Good-by. I'll see you tomorrow."

"We'll go looking for food in the morning," called Paul.

Betsy waved. "I'll see you then."

Homer and Barney and Paul stood and watched her go skipping out of the yard.

"Well, we're snake partners," said Homer. They all began to laugh.

"Crazy way to get a snake," said Paul.

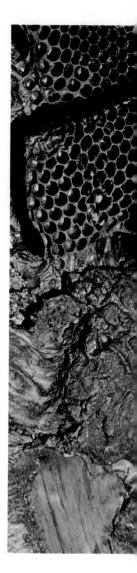

AUGUST
AUTHOR
━━━━━

You might like to know more about Miriam Schlein, the lady who wrote *The Snake in the Carpool.*

Miriam Schlein was born and grew up in Brooklyn, New York. When she finished college, she worked for a book publishing company. Then she decided to try writing books herself. Her first success was a book called *Shapes,* and she has been a well-known writer for boys and girls ever since then. She is married to a sculptor, Harvey Weiss, who also writes books for young people.

Other books written by Miriam Schlein that you might enjoy are *Amazing Mr. Pelgrew, Deer in the Snow, The Raggle-Taggle Fellow,* and *Amuny, Boy of Old Egypt.*

SEPTEMBER

The breezes taste
   Of apple peel.
The air is full
   Of smells to feel—
Ripe fruit, old footballs,
   Burning brush,
New books, erasers,
   Chalk, and such.
The bee, his hive
   Well-honeyed, hums,
And Mother cuts
   Chrysanthemums.
Like plates washed clean
   With suds, the days
Are polished with
   A morning haze.

               – John Updike

ANTEATERS....

How would you like to have this animal for a pet? A pet anteater would surely be most helpful to have along on a picnic!

Many kinds of animals eat ants and other insects, but there is just one family of animals that are true Anteaters.

The largest and best-known of the true Anteaters is the Great Anteater that lives in the warm countries of Central and South America. This anteater is about the size of a small bear. It has long hair and a very bushy tail. At the end of its long, pointed head is a mouth that is only about the size of a raisin. The Great Anteater has no teeth. Instead, it catches insects with its long, sticky tongue.

Great Anteaters live in shady forests. They don't like to fight other animals. They usually use their long claws only to scratch for insects, but they will use them for fighting if they are cornered.

Let me tell you about Arthur...

by Bernard Waber

First, I will tell you what Arthur is like
most of the time.

Most of the time, Arthur is a kind,
helpful,
understanding,
well-behaved,
orderly,
loving,
loveable,
altogether
wonderful son.

BUT...

sometimes,
Arthur is a problem.
Not all of the time, mind you,
just sometimes.
I will explain.

Sometimes Arthur has nothing to do.

"I have nothing to do," says Arthur.

"Why don't you call on a friend?" I suggest.

"Who?" Arthur asks.

"How about William?"

"William is not my friend."

"How about Thomas?"

"Thomas is not feeling well."

"How about Patrick?"

"Patrick is being punished."

"How about Bertram?"

"Bertram is having company."

"How about Maria?"

"Who?"

"Maria."

"Maria is a girl."

"So?"

"So I don't play with girls."

"Maria can throw a ball," I mention.

"She throws like a girl."

"Why don't you read a book?"

"I have read all of my books."

"How about playing records?"

"The record player is broken."

"You can work with your microscope."

"I did that this morning."

"Well," I say, "I have one more suggestion. Since you have nothing to do, and I have much to do, you can spend the day helping me."

"Doing what?" Arthur asks.

"Well, there are things to be carried up to the attic. The shelves in the kitchen need straightening. The garden could be weeded. And..."

Arthur puts on his hat and jacket.

"Where are you going?" I ask.

"I think I will go and see what Maria is doing," he answers.

Sometimes Arthur is choosy.

"Breakfast! Breakfast is ready!"
I call to Arthur.

Arthur comes down.

"What are we having?" he asks.

"We are having ants," I answer.

"What kind of ants?"

"The red ones," I tell him.

Arthur makes a face.

I pretend not to notice.

40

"Look at them," I say in my cheeriest voice.
"Aren't these the most beautiful ants
you have ever seen ... in all your life?
I gathered them just for you."

Arthur looks and makes another face.

"Arthur," I go on, "red ants are delicious,
and so good for you, too. Don't you want
to grow up to be big and strong — as big and
as strong as your father? Have you watched
your father eat red ants?"

More faces from Arthur.

"I have an idea," I say.
"How about if I sprinkle
sugar on them?
Red ants are simply
delightful with sugar."
Arthur shakes his head.
"A twist of lemon, perhaps?"
More head shaking from Arthur.

"Arthur, red ants aren't exactly easy to come by!" I remind him. "You have to scratch mighty deep for red ants!"

Arthur begins playing with his spoon.

"You ought to at least try one," I continue. "You will never know if you like something unless you give it a chance. Here, how about this one?"

"Ilk!" says Arthur, turning his head away.

"Very well!" I exclaim at last. "Never mind about the red ants. Never mind that you are missing out on the world's tastiest, most delicious dish. What will you eat instead?"

"Brown ants," Arthur answers.

Sometimes Arthur forgets.

"Good-by," says Arthur,
rushing off to school.
"Good-by," I say.
The door closes.
The door opens.
"What did you forget?" I ask.
"I forgot my spelling book,"
he answers.
Up he runs,
two steps at a time.
Down he comes with
his spelling book.
"Good-by,"
says Arthur.
"Good-by," I say.
The door closes.

The door opens.

"What did you forget?" I ask.

"I forgot my sneakers," he answers.

Up he runs, two steps at a time.

Down he comes with his sneakers.

"Good-by," says Arthur.

"Good-by," I say.

The door closes.

 The door opens.

 "What did you forget?" I ask.

 "I forgot my pencil case," he answers.

 Up he runs, two steps at a time.

 Down he comes with his pencil case.

"Arthur," I say to him, "you have to try to remember not to forget. Now stop and think. Do you have everything you need?"

"Yes," Arthur answers.

"You are absolutely, without a shade of a doubt, one hundred percent sure now?"

"Yes, I am absolutely, without a shade of a doubt, one hundred percent sure," he answers.

"Good-by then."

"Good-by," says Arthur.

The door closes.

I wait to see if it will open again.

I am not disappointed.

The door opens.

"What did you forget?" I ask.

"I forgot to kiss you good-by,"
he answers.

"Good-by," says Arthur.

"Good-by," I say.

The door closes.

See what I mean
about Arthur?

This is only part of Bernard Waber's book, An Anteater Named Arthur. *You can find out more about Arthur and his mother by reading the rest of the book.*

AUTHOR

Bernard Waber writes books for boys and girls and also works for *Life* magazine. He was born and grew up in Philadelphia, Pennsylvania, and he now lives on Long Island, New York, with his wife and three children.

Mr. Waber is well known for his delightful stories about animals who act very much like people. Several years ago, he wrote *The House on East 88th Street,* the story of a crocodile named Lyle who lived with a family in a New York apartment. The book was chosen an Honor Book by a New York newspaper, and Lyle the crocodile became famous. Since then Mr. Waber has written other "Lyle" books: *Lyle, Lyle, Crocodile, Lyle and the Birthday Party,* and *Lovable Lyle.* Other books by Mr. Waber that you will enjoy are *Rich Cat, Poor Cat, A Rose for Mr. Bloom,* and *"You Look Ridiculous," Said the Rhinoceros to the Hippopotamus.*

I've heard you hundreds of times. Now I know what you look like.

STRANGE WORD

Skill Lesson 1:

FIGURING OUT NEW WORDS

You're sure to meet words in your reading that you haven't seen before or don't remember. Most of them will be words you would know if you heard them. Many will be words you've used yourself in talking. You just don't recognize them in print. But you can usually figure them out for yourself if you do these three things:

1. Think what the other words are saying.

2. Then think the sounds you know for the consonant letters in the word as you look at them in left-to-right order. Usually you will need to think a sound for a vowel only when that vowel comes at the beginning of a word.

3. Decide what word that has those consonant sounds in that order would make good sense with the other words.

The words in heavy black letters in the following paragraph may be words you haven't seen before:

When Bobby came in from play, he could sniff the **odor** of something cooking. It was a **pleasant** smell to Bobby who was feeling hungry. He was **eager** for dinner time to come. That must be why he didn't even make a face when his mother **expected** him to help his sister set the table.

Look at the first word in heavy black letters, and think what the other words are saying. Notice that this word begins with a vowel, so you need to think of a sound for that vowel. You probably know that when just one consonant comes between two vowels, the first vowel often stands for its long sound. The long *o* sound is the sound you hear at the beginning of *old*. If you think of the sounds that *d* and *r* stand for coming after the long *o* sound, you will know what the word is.

Look at the second word, and think what the other words are saying. Then think the sounds you know for the consonants *p, l, s, n,* and *t* in that order. As soon as you do that, you'll know what the word is. You shouldn't have to try different sounds for the letters *ea,* or worry about what sound to think for the *a.*

Look at the third word, and think what the other

words are saying. This word begins with a pair of vowels. You know that the vowels *ea* stand for many different sounds in different words. But you also know that they stand for the long *e* sound more often than any other. As soon as you think the long *e* sound, and then the sounds for *g* and *r,* you will know what the word is and that it makes good sense there.

Look at the last word in heavy black letters. Think what the other words are saying. You should know the sounds for the common syllables at the beginning and end of that word and for the consonants *p, c,* and *t.* If you think those sounds in the right order, you'll know the word that makes good sense there.

Discussion

If you are asked to do so, read aloud one of the sentences about Bobby. Tell how you decided what the word in heavy black letters is.

Help others answer these questions:

1. What three things should you do when you meet a word you don't already know? When will you most often need to think a sound for a vowel?

2. In which word did it help to notice only one consonant between vowels? Why?

3. In which word did knowing two common syllables help? What are those common syllables?

4. In the word *pleasant,* there is a pair of vowels that stands for several different sounds in different words. What told you which was the right sound to use for the letters in *pleasant?* What told you what sound to use for those same letters in *eager?*

On your own

In the following paragraph, use the sense of what is being said and what you know about the sounds that letters stand for to figure out for yourself any word you don't already know:

> Bobby was certain he was going to enjoy his dinner. And he wasn't at all dissatisfied. The first thing he had was his favorite kind of soup: tomato soup. That was followed by a tender slice of pork, a baked potato, carrots, and applesauce. To top it all off, his mother served chocolate cake. Bobby had several pieces of that. His father said, "What a tremendous appetite you have, young man!"

Checking your work

If you are asked to do so, read aloud one of the sentences about Bobby's dinner. If any of the words in the sentence were new to you, tell which they were and how you figured them out by yourself.

Whizz-a-roo Pitch

by Avis Demmitt

"Gram!" Debby shouted as she dashed off the train toward her grandmother. "I thought I'd never get here."

"Debby Mason!" Grandmother said. She kissed Debby's cheek. "My land! You're almost a young lady."

"No, not yet, thank goodness," said Debby's grandfather as she turned to hug him, too. "You still playing ball, Debs?"

"I certainly am," Debby said. "And I'm pitcher again, Gramps. We've won all but one game so far this year. Don't you think it's time for you to teach me your whizz-a-roo pitch?"

"Oh, now, you two!" Mrs. Mason scolded. "Forget baseball for a while. We'd better get home. I left a roast in the oven."

When they were in the car, headed for the farm, Mr. Mason turned to wink at Debby. "We'll have to stir up some excitement. Maybe we can round up some of the neighborhood kids and have a ball game."

"The peaches are nearly ripe," Gram said. "The pickers are to come the day after tomorrow. Debby will want to help pick."

"Oh, yes!" Debby said. "I've never been here at the right time before. I want to ride Buckskin, too."

The car stopped beside a white farmhouse.

"There's Jack!" Debby cried as she hopped out of the car. She patted the big black and white dog's head. "And here comes Tiger," she added when she saw the old yellow cat.

Debby helped Gram with supper and with the dishes. Bedtime came much too soon. The next morning Gramps waited while she helped with the dishwashing, and then he took her to the orchard.

"What do you think of those peaches?" he asked.

Debby gasped. "Gramps, I never saw such giant peaches. They're bigger than baseballs!"

"Those are my new prize trees," Gramps said. "I'm really going to make money on them. A fellow drove in here a few days ago to look at the orchard. He wanted to buy all the peaches I had, and he offered me a very good price for them."

"Are they as good as they look?" Debby asked.

Mr. Mason reached up and picked one. "Try it," he said. "We'll start picking these tomorrow morning. But you may eat all you want. Now let's play ball. I want to see how much you've improved since last summer."

"How about that whizz-a-roo pitch you used when you played with the Detroit Tigers?" Debby asked. "Will you show me how to throw it?"

"When I think you're ready for it," Gramps said. "Now show me what you can do."

He tossed the ball to her. Debby tried her best, throwing the ball fast and hard.

"That's enough practice for today." Gramps patted her shoulder. "Best girl pitcher I ever saw," he said. "I think you need a little more practice before you're ready for the whizz-a-roo. But we'll work hard while you are here, and maybe you'll be ready before you go home."

Debby tried to hide her disappointment. She picked up the ball and turned toward the house.

"I'd better see if Gram needs my help," she said. "I'll keep working on the pitching, Gramps.

May I have another of those prize peaches this afternoon?"

"All you want," Gramps told her. "Just watch out for that big hornets' nest on the fourth tree. See it? I'll spray the nest this evening."

They got to the house in time for Debby to set the table for lunch. After they ate, Gramps went to look over the cornfield.

"You'll have to stay with Gramps this afternoon," Gram said to Debby. "I have a meeting today, but I'll be home by five."

"Don't worry, Gram," Debby told her. "When Gramps gets back, we'll practice ball again."

Thirty minutes later, she stood at the gate and watched Gram drive away. Gramps had not come back. Then she saw him coming from the field. He was running.

"Bad grass fire over at Shaw's farm," he shouted. "Help me wet some sacks. I'll have to go to help fight it. Tell Gram where I've gone."

Debby rushed to help. She dipped the sacks into the big tank of water and carried them to the pickup truck. After it had left, she remembered that Gram was gone, too. She was alone.

"Oh, well," she said. "I'll get some books and pick some peaches to eat."

Debby sat down in the shade back of the old toolshed. She had just started to read when she heard a car. She peeked around the corner of the shed and saw a truck drive into the orchard. "It must be some of the pickers," she thought.

Three men got out of the truck, each with baskets and ladder. They headed straight for the prize peach trees.

"Make it snappy!" one of them called. "The old lady is gone for the afternoon. And the old man will be busy with that fire for some time. We should be able to clean them up."

"Why, they're stealing our peaches!" Debby gasped. "What am I going to do? If I go around the shed to the house, they'll see me. I can't get to the phone. How can I stop them?"

Then, as she peeked around the corner again, she saw the hornets' nest. Slowly her hand closed on one of the peaches she had picked. Carefully she edged away from the shed, still keeping it between her and the three thieves. She aimed carefully.

WHAM! The peach missed the nest by about four inches. "Gramps was right," Debby thought unhappily. "I'm not good enough."

"What was that?" called one of the men.

"Just a peach falling," another answered. "Get busy."

Debby was shaking. What if they found her? What would they do to her? Suddenly her glance fell on the ball she had tossed down by the shed that morning. She picked it up and again aimed carefully.

WHIZZ! The ball slammed into the hornets' nest. Debby could hear the wild, angry buzzing. She slipped into the shed and closed the door.

A moment later she heard cries of pain. Then came the sounds of running feet. Debby peeped

out of the window in time to see the thieves climb
into the truck and speed away. She got a good
look at the license number as they backed the
truck.

The moment the truck had gone, Debby
dashed back to the house and called the sheriff.

Gramps came back two hours later, tired and dirty. "That fire was set," he said to Debby. "Someone used gasoline to start it."

Debby grinned at him. "Never mind, Gramps," she told him. "The men who did it are in jail. They set the fire so that they could steal your prize peaches while you were fighting it."

"What's that!" Gramps shouted.

Debby told him what had happened. She showed him the tracks of the truck and the ladders and baskets that the thieves had left behind. The hornets had swarmed back to their tree.

Gramps looked at Debby proudly. "A real pitcher!" he exclaimed. "I'll be proud to teach you that old whizz-a-roo pitch. We'll get at it first thing in the morning."

AUTHOR

Avis Demmitt was a third-grade teacher in Kansas until she retired. She has always lived in Kansas, but she has traveled to many parts of the world. She is still writing stories for children and is enjoying such hobbies as collecting stamps.

Mrs. Demmitt has had stories published in many children's magazines. "Whizz-a-Roo Pitch" first appeared in *Jack and Jill.* She has also written stories for *Child Life, Wee Wisdom,* and many other magazines.

MR. NOBODY

I know a funny little man,
    As quiet as a mouse.
He does the mischief that is done
    In everybody's house.
Though no one ever sees his face,
    Yet one and all agree
That every plate we break, was cracked
    By Mr. Nobody.

The fingermarks upon the door
    By none of us were made.
We never leave the blinds unclosed
    To let the curtains fade.
The ink we never spill, the boots
    That lying round you see
Are not our boots; they all belong
    To Mr. Nobody.

— Author unknown

WHO NEEDS PUNCH?

by Robin Palmer

"The new baby is a lot easier to take care of than Punch," said Jim Barkington, moving the butter away from his two-year-old brother. "Sometimes I wonder whether we really needed Punch in this family."

"Goodness me!" cried his mother. "As if we could do without any one of you. You used to be just like that when you were little."

The rest of the family laughed. "Well, Jim, now you know," said Roddy. He was the oldest of the five Barkingtons. Next came Jim and then Patsy, who was the only girl. She was seven years old and right in the middle of the family.

Mrs. Barkington wiped some jam off the end of Punch's nose. "Be sure to come straight home after school," she said. "This is Patsy's day to go to the dentist. I'm going downtown with her and taking the baby. You boys can look after Punch."

Jim groaned.

"I'm sure Punch should go to the dentist, too," Roddy said quickly. "He acts as if he's getting another tooth."

Mrs. Barkington didn't seem to hear him. "Run along," she said. "You don't want to be late for school."

The three older children left the table and started down the street.

"It's one of those days when everything goes wrong," Roddy said. "You wait and see."

"Oh, Punch isn't that bad," said Patsy. "The trick is never to let him get out of your sight."

"We know that," answered Roddy coldly. "It means we can't do a single thing all afternoon but sit and look at that baby. Leave him alone for just one minute, and he finds an ink bottle or a box of eggs or something that makes a mess. It's all very well for *you* to talk, Patsy. You don't have to stay with him."

"Would you rather go to the dentist?" asked his sister.

Jim laughed. "Of course not."

That afternoon Roddy and Jim stood at the window and watched the others go down the street. Punch was cheerfully pulling books out of the bookcase.

"What are we going to do with him?" asked Jim.

"We could take turns watching him," Roddy said. "One of us could read while the other watched."

"Who wants to read?" said Jim.

Roddy started to say, "I do," but instead, he stopped and listened. Then he threw open the window. "What's that?" he asked.

A long way off, Jim could hear the sound of bells ringing and whistles blowing. It grew louder and louder. Clang, CLANG, CLANG!

"A fire!" yelled Jim. "Here come the engines."

Roddy leaned out of the window. "It must be near here," he said. "Let's follow the engines."

"What about Punch?"

"Why, we'll take him along. He may never have another chance to see a fire. Come on, Punch."

As he spoke, Roddy grabbed one of Punch's arms, and Jim took the other. Off they went, out

the door and down the block. More engines
passed them as they ran. They could see smoke a
few blocks away. They would have gone faster
if it had not been for Punch. He lifted his feet
from the ground and let his brothers carry him
by the arms.

"Of all the stupid tricks," Roddy puffed.

"If only Mother didn't feed him such a lot,"
Jim complained. "He weighs too much. Put your
feet on the ground, Punch, or I'll drop you."

Punch just giggled.

"He knows you won't," grunted Roddy.

They went on, hurrying as much as they could,
until they got to the block where the fire was. It

was crowded with people. Firemen had tied ropes across the street to hold back the crowd.

"If we could just wriggle through the crowd," said Roddy, "we might be able to see something."

Roddy let go of Punch's arm. "Jim can hold him," he thought, "while I find a good place to stand."

At almost the same instant, Jim had the same idea. "If I were on the other side of this man," he said to himself, "I could see something. Roddy will hang on to Punch." So he let go of his brother, too.

Punch was so small he could see even less than Jim and Roddy. In front of his nose was the wide blackness of a woman's coat. He couldn't see to the top of it, and he couldn't see to the side of it. He looked down at the pavement. His only chance to go forward was to get on his hands and knees, so down he went.

Punch was used to crawling, even in tight places. In and out he went, around one pair of feet after another, until he was in the very front row. Then he went under the rope.

No one noticed Punch. He stopped for a minute wondering what to do next. Then he saw a small kitten. Punch liked cats. He crawled toward it, right up to the building where the fire was!

Sudden Pride

The older boys didn't get through the crowd so easily. Jim wriggled and squeezed with all his might. He was squeezed between a tall man and a very fat woman. He couldn't see the fire any better than before. He felt as if all the air were being pressed out of him. It was a tight feeling.

"No use staying here," he thought. "I'll pull out and find Roddy."

Pulling out was harder than it sounded. In fact, it was just as much of a squeeze as pushing in. But Jim did it. He backed away from the crowd and took a deep breath. Then he saw Roddy running toward him.

"Where's Punch?" cried Roddy.

Jim had forgotten all about Punch. "I don't know," he answered. "I thought you had him!"

"But I left him with you!" gasped Roddy. "Where on earth do you suppose he is?"

"It's only been a minute or two," Jim said. "He can't have gone far. Let's call him."

They walked up and down, shouting, "Punch! Punch! Come here." But Punch didn't come.

A man in the crowd turned to look at the boys. "Did you lose your dog?" he asked.

"No," cried Roddy. "It's our little brother! He's not three years old yet. Have you seen him?"

"No, I haven't," replied the man, "but I'll try to help you."

He spoke to other people in the crowd. "There is a little boy lost," he said. "Has anyone seen him?"

One after another, they began to look, but the answer was always the same. "No, he isn't here. He isn't here."

"Where can he have gone?" Jim wondered.

"Let the boys through," one man said. Some of the people stepped back and others moved aside so that Jim and Roddy could get right up to the rope.

"Oh dear," cried Jim. "If only I had held on to him! What will we do? What will we do, Roddy?"

"He must be here," answered his brother. "He — oh, look!"

Jim gave a shout. One of the firemen was coming toward them. He had Punch in his arms, and Punch was hugging a little cat.

The boys crawled under the rope and started to run across the street to him. But before they had gone three steps, they felt a pull on their collars. A voice asked, "Where do you think you're going?"

They looked around at the blue coat and brass buttons of a big policeman. "Don't you know what that rope is for?" he asked.

"Yes," answered Roddy, "but the fireman has our baby brother. Please let us go to him, sir."

The policeman had his back toward Punch and couldn't see him. He said, "A likely story!"

Roddy cried, "Really, it's true. Mother had to take Patsy downtown to the dentist, so she left us to look after Punch. But now we've lost him in the crowd."

The policeman still looked doubtful.

At that moment, Punch saw his brothers and waved to them.

"Look," Roddy said. "Look over there, if you don't believe us."

The policeman turned around. "For goodness sake!" he exclaimed. Then he took the boys across the street.

Punch smiled sweetly at them. "Kitty," he said. "Got kitty."

"He saved the little cat," explained the fireman. "Isn't he a fine boy? I wish he were mine."

"He's ours," said Roddy. There was a sudden note of pride in his voice.

"Their mother is at the dentist's," the policeman said. He took Punch from the fireman and handed him over to his brothers. "Run along now," he told them. "It isn't safe for you to stay here."

The boys held Punch firmly. They took one last look at the fire before they started to make their way through the crowd.

"Look at that baby," they heard someone say. "He saved that little kitten. What a brave child!"

"You have a fine little brother," said an old lady. "You must be very proud of him."

People tried to pat Punch on the head. All of a sudden, even Jim felt that his brother was quite worth having.

"I wish he could tell us all about it!" Jim said, as they hurried along home. "But anyway, I'm glad he saved the little kitten."

AUTHOR

"Who Needs Punch?" is one of many stories that Robin Palmer has written about the Barkington family. At one time they were published in a book called *The Barkingtons*, which you may still be able to find in your library.

Robin Palmer was the youngest child in a large family. The family lived in an apartment house in New York City. Even though their home was pretty crowded, they always managed to have a cat and a dog. They also kept other strange pets, such as the tadpoles which grew into frogs and had to play in the bathtub! No doubt the author got many of her story ideas from things that happened in her early life. She is now married and has children of her own.

Other books by Robin Palmer that you may enjoy reading are *Ship's Dog*, *Wise House*, and *Dragons, Unicorns, and Other Magical Beasts*.

Nobody Loves Me

Somedays,
nobody loves me
so I go down the names
I know:

    I hate Martha

    I hate James

    I hate Selma

    I hate Jo.

Nobody likes me,
that I know.

Somedays,
everyone loves me
so I go down the names
I know:

    I love Martha

    I love James

    I love Selma

    I love Jo.

Everyone loves me,
I know so!

      – *Charlotte Zolotow*

Skill Lesson 2:

GETTING MEANING FROM CONTEXT

Sometimes in your reading, you meet a word you've seen and read before, but none of the meanings you know for that word make good sense with the other words.

Many words have more than one meaning. For example, you know what a dog's bark is and what the bark of a tree is, but that wouldn't help you understand the word *bark* in these sentences:

Jack liked to make tiny make-believe airplanes and ships. The one that had taken him the longest to put together was a bark.

By the time you reached the word *bark,* you knew that it couldn't have anything to do with either dogs or trees. But what was said before the word tells you that there must be a bark that is either some kind of airplane or some kind of ship. The next two sentences would tell you a lot more. Here they are:

Now that all its sails were in place, it made Jack think of the stories he'd read about the old days. In those days, seamen had worried when the wind stopped blowing.

Those sentences would let you know that a bark was a kind of sailing ship that was used long ago before men found out how to make ships move through water without help from the wind.

Notice that you figured out the meaning of *bark* by thinking what would make sense with the rest of what is being said. Sometimes what is said before the word will help. Sometimes you can get help from what is said after the word, and often you will get help from what is said both before and after. That is called **using the context to get the meaning of a word.**

Now suppose that the word *brigantine* had been used instead of *bark.* Probably you have never heard that word and have no meaning at all for it. But by using the context, you could teach yourself that a brigantine was a special kind of old-time sailing ship.

When you meet a printed word that you don't know

the meaning of, whether or not you know how to pronounce it, use the context to help you figure out the meaning. The parts of the context that can help you may be single words, short groups of words, or sentences. The helpful parts may come before or after or both before and after the word.

Discussion

Help your class answer these questions:

1. Why do you sometimes need to figure out the meaning of a word you already know?
2. What is meant by using the context to get the meaning of a word?
3. What may the helpful parts of the context be? Where may they appear?
4. What parts of the context helped you most to get the meaning of *bark?*

On your own

As you read the paragraph that follows, use the context to help you figure out the meaning of any word in heavy black print that you do not already know.

Bob seemed to have a **bent** for getting into trouble. One day he **deceived** his friends into thinking he had drowned. He did this by swimming away from them under water and **concealing** himself in some bushes. His friends ran to tell his mother. She believed them and was, of course, broken-hearted. In her **anguish,** she called the police and begged them to see what they could do. The police found Bob getting dressed. When he told what he'd done, they gave him a **severe** scolding for playing such a trick. But you can imagine his mother's **relief** when she saw that Bob was perfectly **sound.**

Checking your work

If you are asked to do so, explain what one of the words in heavy black letters means. Then tell which parts of the context helped you decide what that meaning is.

FALLING LEAVES

As I was going out to play,
I saw the first leaf fall today.
I watched it fall without a sound
Until it rested on the ground.

Another leaf soon left the tree.
It fell and came to rest on me . . .
An orange leaf with bits of brown.
I smoothed it out and pressed it down.

Then more leaves, orange, brown, and red,
Came flying down around my head.
They made a soft pile on the street,
A leafy carpet for my feet.

Carefully I looked around
At all the bright leaves on the ground.
I picked the best leaf of them all
To keep a little bit of fall.

— M. Caporale Shecktor
and Harriet May Savitz

79

HIGH, WIDE, AND HANDSOME

In a village on the road to Pegu, there lived three friends: High, a monkey; Wide, a pig; and Handsome, a fox.

High, Wide, and Handsome were the laziest fellows in the countryside. While everyone else was working very hard, they lay on the porch of the village rest house, telling stories and drinking palm juice.

High, Wide, and Handsome liked to hang around the rest house. There was always a chance that a traveler would treat them to a nice dinner in return for a story.

One day a hound drove up to the rest house. His name was Rolling Stone. Rolling Stone had a yellow sports car and was dressed in the most beautiful clothes that High, Wide, and Handsome had ever seen.

A Burmese folktale

and Their Three Tall Tales

High, Wide, and Handsome stared at the splendid stranger.

"Oh, those velvet slippers!" sighed High.

"Oh, those fancy trousers!" sighed Wide.

"That feathered hat and that walking stick!" said Handsome.

The clothes that High, Wide, and Handsome wore looked very ordinary beside Rolling Stone's.

High, Wide, and Handsome tiptoed around Rolling Stone as he was drinking palm juice on the porch.

High whispered to Wide, "Do you think we can get him to treat us to a nice lunch?"

"I have a better idea," said Handsome. "Let us trick him into giving us his beautiful clothes."

"How?" said Wide.

Handsome whispered his plan to his friends. They agreed that it was a very good plan.

by Jean Merrill

When Rolling Stone had finished his juice and was ready to travel on, Handsome went up to him. Handsome said, "Why travel in the heat of the day? Stay and have lunch with me and my friends."

"Why, thank you very much," said Rolling Stone. "I will."

High, Wide, and Handsome treated Rolling Stone to a fine lunch. Then, after lunch, everyone stretched out on the porch to rest.

While they were resting, Handsome said, "Let us make a bet to see who can tell the most unusual story."

"All right," said Rolling Stone. "But how shall we judge which is the most unusual story?"

"The story must be so unusual," High said, "that someone says, 'I don't believe it!'"

"You mean that if I tell a story so unusual that you do not believe it, I will win the bet?" asked Rolling Stone.

"That's right," said Wide.

"And will there be a prize for the winner?" asked Rolling Stone.

"Of course," said Handsome. "Whoever loses must work for the winner and do whatever the winner orders him to do."

"That is a bet worth winning," said Rolling Stone.

High, Wide, and Handsome were certain that one of the stories they were going to tell would make Rolling Stone forget himself and exclaim, "I don't believe it!" Then he would lose the bet, and they would order him to give them his clothes.

"I will begin," said High. With his eye on Rolling Stone's velvet slippers, High began to tell his story:

"Last week," said High, "I got in my boat and
went fishing. I was having very bad luck, and I
asked some other fishermen how they were doing.

"They told me that they had not caught anything,
either. So I decided to see what was going on at
the bottom of the river. I dived into the water, and
it was three days before I touched bottom.

"When I got there, I discovered that a fish as big as a mountain was eating up all the other fish. I killed this monster fish with one blow.

"Then, as I was hungry, I built a fire and roasted the monster and ate him at one sitting. After that I floated back to the top, got in my boat, and came home."

When High had finished his story, he looked around slyly to see what Rolling Stone would say.

Rolling Stone showed no surprise. "Thank you," he said. "I like fishing stories. And what a clever fisherman you are."

"Now I shall tell a story," said Wide.

Wide could hardly wait to see himself in Rolling Stone's trousers, though he did wonder whether the trousers might not be a little tight for him.

They could be stretched, he decided. And he began to tell his story:

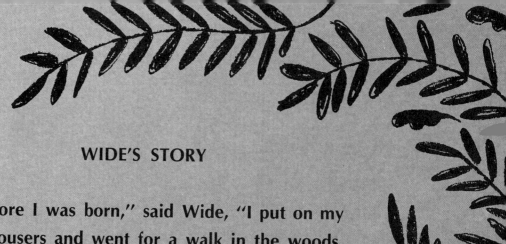

WIDE'S STORY

"Before I was born," said Wide, "I put on my best trousers and went for a walk in the woods. I came upon a tamarind tree a thousand feet high.

"The ripe tamarinds looked delicious. So I climbed the tree and ate until I was full. By then I was so heavy and sleepy that I could not climb down.

"Naturally, I was terribly afraid that I would fall out of the tree and hurt myself. So I ran back to the village and got a ladder.

"Then I put the ladder up against the tree and climbed safely down."

Wide nearly burst out laughing at his own story. He looked at Rolling Stone, expecting the hound to say, "I don't believe it!"

But Rolling Stone showed no surprise. "You were clever to think of a ladder," he said. "Or you might still be up in the tamarind tree."

Then it was Handsome's turn to tell a story.

Handsome could see himself with the walking stick and the feathered hat. He began his story:

"When I was only a year old," said Handsome, "I was chasing a rabbit. The rabbit ran into a thicket, and I ran after it.

"But as I was about to grab it, the rabbit turned into a tiger. It was the biggest tiger I had ever seen.

"The tiger roared and opened his mouth to swallow me. I told him that it would be quite unfair of him to eat me, as I had been looking for a rabbit, not a tiger.

"But the tiger paid no attention. As he came toward me, I caught hold of his jaw and gave it a jerk. To my surprise, the tiger broke in two and died."

Rolling Stone did not look surprised at all. "That poor tiger," he said. "What a clever hunter you are."

"I don't know many stories," Rolling Stone went on. "While you fellows have been hunting and fishing and eating tamarinds, I have been working at one job or another.

"However," he said, "here is a story that you may find hard to believe."

Rolling Stone cleared his throat and began to tell his story:

"Some years ago," said Rolling Stone, "I bought a coconut farm, and on this farm grew a very strange coconut tree. It was of a bright red color and grew no higher than a bush. For a long time this tree had no branches and no leaves.

"One day I decided to chop it down. But just as I lifted my ax, three branches suddenly appeared. The branches had no leaves, but there was a coconut on each branch.

"I was about to pick the coconuts, when they burst open, and a pig jumped out of one, a fox from the second, and a monkey from the third.

"As the pig and the fox and the monkey came from my coconuts, they belonged to me, so I made them work on my farm.

"But they ran away, and I have been looking for them ever since. Now, at last, I have found them. You know very well that you are my run-away pig, fox, and monkey! Now you must pack at once and come back to my farm with me."

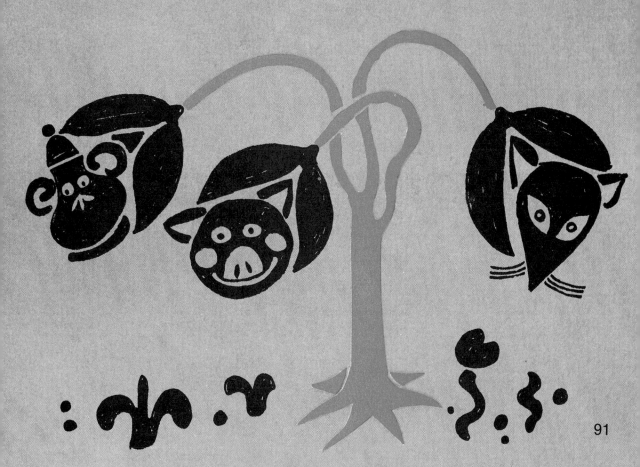

High, Wide, and Handsome looked at each other in amazement. If they said that they believed Rolling Stone's story, they would be agreeing that they belonged to him and would have to work for him.

But if they said they *didn't* believe his story, he would win the bet — and they would have to do anything he ordered them to do!

"Speak up," said Rolling Stone. "Do you believe my story — or don't you?"

High, Wide, and Handsome did not know what to say.

"Very well," laughed Rolling Stone. "No matter how you answer, I win the bet!"

Then Rolling Stone waved his walking stick and said, "I order you to give me the clothes you are wearing. Take them off, fold them neatly, and put them in my car."

High, Wide, and Handsome had no choice. They took off their clothes and put them in Rolling Stone's car.

"And now," said Rolling Stone. "You are free to go. For I am going to give up farming."

And with that, he tipped his hat, jumped into his car, and disappeared in a cloud of dust.

AUTHOR

Jean Merrill was born in Rochester, New York, and has traveled all over the world. Once she took a bicycle trip through Europe, visiting ten countries. Another time she was sent by the United States Government to study folktales and folk art at the University of Madras in India. While she was there, she also visited the country of Burma, where she heard the tale *High, Wide, and Handsome*. Another of her books, *Shan's Lucky Knife*, is also a Burmese folktale.

Miss Merrill has written many books for young people. Some of them are *The Superlative Horse, Emily Emerson's Moon, The Black Sheep*, and, for older boys and girls, the popular *Pushcart War*.

AT THE SEA-SIDE

When I was down beside the sea,
A wooden spade they gave to me
To dig the sandy shore.

My holes were empty like a cup.
In every hole the sea came up,
Till it could come no more.

– Robert Louis Stevenson

THE WIND

At evening when I play about,
The wind keeps coming by.
There must be miles and miles of it
Like ribbon in the sky.

I think it must be rolled upon
A great big giant spool
That someone unwinds yard by yard
To keep us nice and cool.

— *Frances Duggar*

95

The FRIENDLY GHOST

by Elizabeth Yates

Julie had never been away from home before, and her first night in the country was a frightening one. Of course, she knew Aunt Anna and Uncle Harry well, for they had often come to the city to visit her parents. But this was the first time she had been at the farm.

Julie wasn't at all sure that she was going to like making friends with horses and cows and chickens. She wished she hadn't come. She wished she could go home tomorrow. Julie put her hands up to her eyes. She didn't want to cry. She was nine years old now, and that was much too old to cry. But she did feel lonely and strange as she stood in the middle of her room before she got ready for bed.

There was a knock at the door. "May I come in, Julie? I've got something for you." It was Uncle Harry's cheerful voice.

"Ye-es," Julie said, trying to smile.

"I've brought you some apple[s] [in case you get] hungry in the night." Uncle H[enry came in] with three polished red apples [and set them on the] table by the window. "They're [from the new] crop. I just picked them tod[ay. Aren't they] beauties?"

"Ye-es," Julie said.

Harry looked out the window of the small ...d-floor bedroom. "I used to have this room ...en I was a boy," he said. "I always liked it because I could watch the horses and cows in the pasture. How would you like to ride one of the horses sometime, Julie?"

Julie clapped her hands together. "I'd like that."

Uncle Harry nodded. "Ned is the steadiest one, but Daisy is all right if she likes you."

"How would I know if she liked me?"

"Oh, you'll know all right. She'll come right up to you."

After Uncle Harry left the room, Julie began to think that life in the country might not be so lonely after all. She undressed quickly and had just got into bed when Aunt Anna came in to say good night.

"Sleep well, darling, and don't be alarmed if you hear noises in the night. An old house creaks now and then."

"Why?" Julie asked.

"It's just the way the boards have of talking to themselves, telling about the things they've seen."

"Does it mean there are ghosts?"

"Oh, no," Aunt Anna laughed. "Whoever put such an idea into your head!"

But long after Aunt Anna left the room, Julie wondered about that. She lay wide awake in the darkness. The air coming in the window near the head of her bed ruffled the light curtains. Outside there were crickets and katydids singing, but inside everything was quiet — or almost quiet.

Now and then a board in the floor gave out a small sound, and another one in the wall would answer it. Julie shut her eyes tight, not wanting to see what might be in her room, but quite sure that something was. A cold little shiver began to run down her spine.

Julie opened her eyes for a moment, daring herself to look, but in the darkness she could see nothing. She wished that morning would come soon. Then she thought that she would eat one of the apples Uncle Harry had put on the table by her bed.

She sat up and reached out her hand. Just as she did, she heard a thump outside the window. And then, right in front of her eyes, she could see the curtains of the window move, very slowly. Something long and thin and white reached into the room across the table by the window. Julie screamed and pulled the bedclothes over her. Then she dove down to the foot of the bed.

Aunt Anna and Uncle Harry heard the muffled screams of the little girl and came running down the stairs. They switched on the light in Julie's room and threw back the bedcovers.

"It was a ghost. I know it was," Julie said, her teeth chattering as she tried to tell them what had happened.

Aunt Anna explained to Julie that there weren't any such things as ghosts except in people's imaginations.

Uncle Harry laughed. "Well, I guess I know one little girl who shouldn't eat apples before she goes to sleep."

"But I d-didn't eat an apple," Julie insisted. "I was just g-going to."

"That's funny," Uncle Harry said. "I'm sure I put three apples on the plate, and now there are only two."

Aunt Anna stared at the plate. "Perhaps you ate one yourself, Harry. I certainly polished three apples."

Julie shook her head back and forth. "I know I didn't eat one," she said.

Aunt Anna sat on the edge of Julie's bed. "I'll stay here with you until you fall asleep." Uncle Harry said good night and left the room.

Aunt Anna and Julie talked for a while. Then suddenly Julie pressed Aunt Anna's hand tightly. "What's that?"

"Just a board in the floor," Aunt Anna answered. "You'll get used to sounds like that in an old house."

Julie felt better, but she didn't close her eyes again for a while. She watched the curtains as they fluttered at the window. She was not afraid now. Before long Julie fell asleep.

At breakfast, they all laughed about the strange visitor. Even Julie found it quite easy to joke about ghosts in daylight. Uncle Harry said it must have been a dream, and Aunt Anna said it was probably Julie's imagination. But none of them could explain why there were only two apples left when there had been three on the plate.

Aunt Anna finally said, "You must have eaten one in your sleep, dear."

Julie shook her head. If she had, where were the core and the seeds?

More Apples Disappear

That day Julie helped Aunt Anna in the house, and then she helped Uncle Harry outdoors. She fed the chickens and picked up apples in the orchard. She sat on the pasture fence and watched the two farm horses. She liked Ned, but it was Daisy, the mare, that she hoped her uncle would let her ride.

That evening Julie was quite ready for bed.

Aunt Anna said to Julie, "No ghosts tonight, dear. If you do see or hear anything, remember that it's just the wind at the window or the old boards in the house. There's nothing to fear."

Julie was too tired and far too happy to think about ghosts. She lay in bed with her eyes almost closed, remembering the wonderful day.

When a board creaked in the floor, she smiled

to herself and thought how friendly it was to have a house so old that it could speak. She thought if she listened long enough she might be able to tell what it was saying. But she was much too sleepy tonight to do that.

And then, suddenly, she wasn't sleepy any more. Her eyes that had been half shut were wide open. The curtain began to move at the window. The long white Thing that she had seen the night before came into the room.

Julie didn't waste any time screaming. She shot under the bedcovers. Whatever the Thing was, she had seen it with her own eyes. She was afraid that the next minute it would speak to her. She decided not to take any chances. She kept the covers over her head until morning.

When Aunt Anna came in to wake Julie, she found her curled up at the foot of the bed with the sheets and blankets over her head.

Julie told her what had happened. "It was a ghost," she whispered. "I know it was."

Aunt Anna laughed. "You are a silly little girl. You ought to know that there aren't any such things as ghosts, not in this house anyway."

And then she looked at the plate on the table by the bed and smiled. "Why, Julie, you've eaten another apple! Uncle Harry will be glad that you like them so much."

Julie looked at the table for the first time that morning, and her eyes grew as round as saucers.

The plate had only one apple left on it.

There were pancakes for breakfast. Somehow the mystery of the night didn't seem so bad to Julie as she laughed and talked with her aunt and uncle.

That afternoon, Uncle Harry asked Julie which of the two horses she would rather ride.

"I'd like to ride Daisy," Julie said.

Uncle Harry shook his head. "Daisy doesn't make friends easily, but perhaps she'll be all right with you."

He lifted Julie up onto the white mare's broad
back. Then he got on Ned. They rode off to round
up the cows for the milking. Uncle Harry looked
surprised when he saw how gentle the white
horse was with the little girl.

"I guess you've already been making friends
with old Daisy," he said.

Julie shook her head and ran her hand down
Daisy's neck. She was glad that Uncle Harry
wouldn't have to think she was scared of everything.

They rode around the pasture and brought in
the cows. When they got back to the fence, Julie
was feeling very happy.

That night Julie went bravely to bed. Aunt Anna offered to sleep downstairs with her, but Julie said she would rather not. She felt quite certain now that she must have been dreaming. She knew there couldn't be any ghosts in a house as nice as the one her aunt and uncle lived in. Nobody believed her when she said she hadn't eaten the apples. Julie was so puzzled by their disappearance that she had begun to wonder if perhaps she had eaten them in her sleep — cores, seeds, and all.

"Good night, Julie dear, and I hope you won't have any dreams at all tonight," Aunt Anna said.

Julie was so tired and happy that she didn't spend any time at all lying awake and thinking. Instead she went sound asleep. She would not have awakened before morning if she had not heard a curious sound. Feeling something warm near her face, she opened her eyes.

Moonlight was filling the room. In its soft glow Julie could see clearly that something had put its head in the window. She sat up in bed. A lump of fear rose right into the middle of her throat. She opened her mouth to scream. Then

suddenly she saw who it was. It was her friend
Daisy, on whose broad back she had ridden
around the pasture that afternoon!

Julie put out her hand and stroked the long
gray head. Then she ran her fingers over the
velvet nose.

"Hello, Daisy," she said softly. "That was a
nice ride we had, wasn't it? I hope we can have
one like that every day."

Daisy tossed her head and gave a little whinny.

Julie wished she had a lump of sugar to give
the horse. She explained to Daisy that she would
bring one to her the next morning.

"Do you like apples?" she asked, remembering
that there was one left on the plate.

But when she looked at the plate, she saw that
it was empty!

Slowly a wide smile spread over Julie's face. "I guess you *do* like apples," she said.

Daisy drew her head back from the window and whinnied. Then she flicked her back feet and Julie saw her trotting across the grass.

Uncle Harry and Aunt Anna could hardly believe what Julie had to tell them the next morning at breakfast. But when they went out and saw the hoof marks on the grass, they had to admit that Julie's ghost was only a friendly visitor who liked apples as much as she liked Julie!

AUTHOR

"The Friendly Ghost" is one of Elizabeth Yates's most famous stories. It is also one of her own favorites, for she says that something very much like that happened to her husband when he was a boy.

Elizabeth Yates was born in Buffalo, New York. She went to school in the city but spent her summers on her father's farm. She has always loved farm life and now lives on a farm in New Hampshire.

Elizabeth Yates has won many honors for her writing. Her book, *Amos Fortune, Free Man*, was given the Newbery Medal in 1951. This is one of the greatest honors an author can receive. You might like to learn more about the Newbery Medal and other books that have won it. Other books by Elizabeth Yates that you will also enjoy are *With Pipe, Paddle, and Song, A Place for Peter*, and *Carolina's Courage*.

Oh, there once was a Puffin
Just the shape of a muffin,
And he lived on an island
In the
    bright
        blue
            sea!

He ate little fishes,
That were most delicious,
And he had them for supper
And he
    had
        them
            for tea.

But this poor little Puffin,
He couldn't play nothin',
For he hadn't anybody
To
    play
        with
            at all.

So he sat on his island,
And he cried for awhile, and
He felt very lonely,
And he
    felt
        very
            small.

Then along came the fishes,
And they said, "If you wishes,
You can have us for playmates,
Instead
    of
        for
            tea!"

So they now play together,
In all sorts of weather,
And the puffin eats pancakes,
Like you
    and
        like
            me.
— *Florence Page Jaques*

111

MORE BOOKS TO ENJOY

AUGUST EXPLAINS, *by Phil Ressner and Crosby Bonsall.*
An old bear tells a young bear what it's like to be a human being. The way the young bear tries to picture this will make you laugh.

I MET A MAN, *by John Ciardi.*
These nonsense poems are fun to read.

KEEP YOUR MOUTH CLOSED, DEAR, *by Aliki.*
Charles, a young crocodile, can't seem to help himself: He swallows everything in sight!

MELINDY'S MEDAL, *by Georgene Faulkner and John Becker.*
A quick-thinking girl leads her class to safety when a fire breaks out in school.

MR. RABBIT AND THE LOVELY PRESENT, *by Charlotte Zolotow.*
Mr. Rabbit helps a girl pick out the perfect birthday present for her mother.

THREE BOYS AND SPACE, *by Nan H. Agle and Ellen Wilson.*
This is one book in a popular series about triplets named Abercrombie, Benjamin, and Christopher.

TWO IS A TEAM, *by Jerrold Beim.*
Two boys find that jobs are easier and more fun when they work together.

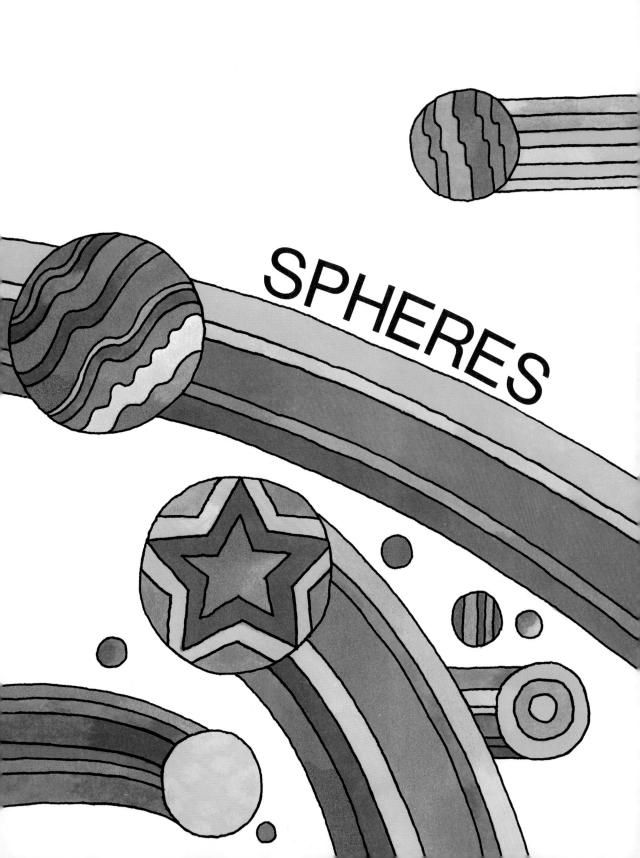

SPHERES

SPHERES

114

THE ANSWERS

"When did the world begin and how?"
I asked a lamb, a goat, a cow.

"What's it all about and why?"
I asked a hog as he passed by.

"How will the whole thing end, and when?"
I asked a duck, a goose, a hen,

And I copied all the answers, too:
A quack, a honk, an oink, a moo!

– ROBERT CLAIRMONT

115

STONE SOUP

BY FAN KISSEN

Adapted from a story by Marcia Brown

Cast

GASTON (GAS-**TAWN**)	SECOND MAN
JEAN (ZHAHN)	SECOND WOMAN
MAYOR	THIRD MAN
FIRST MAN	THIRD WOMAN
FIRST WOMAN	STORYTELLER

STORYTELLER: This is an old folktale called
Stone Soup.

Once upon a time two soldiers were walking
along a country road. They were tired and
hungry. They had spent all their money
in the city and could not buy food or pay for
a room. They wondered what to do.

GASTON: Haven't you any money at all, Jean?

JEAN: Not a bit, Gaston.

GASTON: I'm so hungry I could eat a whole cow!

JEAN: That's the way I feel, too. But even a slice of brown bread would taste good to me now.

GASTON: I'm so tired I could fall asleep standing up.

JEAN: How good it would feel to stretch out in a nice, soft bed!

GASTON: (*Slight pause*) There's a big barn a little way off the road on this side. Let's go in there. The hay will make a soft bed.

JEAN: Wait, Gaston. The owner of the barn must live somewhere near here. If we can find his house, he might give us a bite to eat and a place to sleep indoors.

GASTON: (*Excited*) Oh, look, Jean! There— beyond the barn! There are houses over there!

JEAN: It looks like a small village to me.

GASTON: Let's hurry over, Jean, before it gets dark.

STORYTELLER: Now, a farmer saw the two soldiers walking toward the village. He hurried to spread the news. These villagers didn't like to share their food with anyone. This is how most of the villagers acted when the news reached their homes.

FIRST MAN: (*Quickly*) Listen, wife! I've just heard that two soldiers are coming down the road toward our village!

FIRST WOMAN: (*Upset*) Soldiers! Oh, dear me! They're sure to ask for food. Soldiers eat so much! We must hide our meat!

FIRST MAN: Wrap it in a clean cloth, and I'll hide it in the cellar! Quick, wife! Soldiers walk fast!

SECOND MAN: Two strangers are coming — two soldiers! They might ask for something to eat.

SECOND WOMAN: Oh, dear me! They mustn't see our food! Help me hide our vegetables and bread!

THIRD MAN: Have you heard the news, wife? Two soldiers are on their way to our village! Let's hide our food!

THIRD WOMAN: More soldiers? Goodness! The last ones asked for some milk. These men might want some, too.

THIRD MAN: We must hide these buckets of milk! Help me lower them down into the well! Quickly!

STORYTELLER: The villagers all tried to look as poor and hungry as possible. Soon Gaston and Jean came to the first house at the edge of the village. They knocked at the door.

GASTON: Good evening to you. Can you spare a little food for two hungry soldiers?

FIRST MAN: (*Sad voice*) No, we haven't any food to spare, soldier. We have hardly enough for ourselves and our poor children.

FIRST WOMAN: You'd better go on to the next village. (*Slams door quickly*)

JEAN: Hm! Those children looked pretty healthy to me! Let's try the next house, Gaston. (*Knocks*)

JEAN: Good evening, friend. Can you spare a
    little food for two hungry soldiers?

SECOND MAN: No, we have no food to spare.

SECOND WOMAN: We haven't eaten anything all
    day. (*Slams door quickly*)

GASTON: Huh! I never saw poor, hungry
    people look so well fed! Well, let's try the
    next house. (*Knocks on door*)

JEAN: Good evening, friend. Can you spare a
    little food for two hungry soldiers? We
    haven't eaten all day.

THIRD MAN: No, we have nothing for you. We
    gave all we could spare to some other soldiers
    just a little while ago. (*Slams door*)

STORYTELLER: And so it went. Each door was
    shut in the soldiers' faces. But as soon as Jean
    and Gaston had walked away, each villager
    opened his door again to see what would
    happen at the next house. Soon Gaston and
    Jean had tried every house in the village, but
    no one had given them anything to eat. They
    stopped in the village square and put their
    heads together to think out a plan. Soon they
    thought up a plan they were sure would work.

GASTON: (*Calls loudly*) All you good people at
    your doors! Come, gather around us!

JEAN: We have something important to tell
you!

STORYTELLER: That made the people curious.
They began to leave their houses and walk
to the village square where the two soldiers
were waiting.

GASTON: Listen, my friends! We asked you for
a little food. All of you said you had hardly
enough for yourselves. Well, we're very
sorry for you. *We'll* give *you* some food.
We'll make stone soup for you.

FIRST WOMAN: (*Surprised*) Stone soup? I never
heard of stone soup!

SECOND WOMAN: How do you make stone soup?

GASTON: (*Smiling*) I make it with this smooth, round stone I picked up on the road. But any stone will do. First we'll need a large pot — a very large pot that will hold enough soup for all of you.

MAYOR: Soldier, I'm the Mayor of this village. I'll see that you get a big pot. (*Calls*) Here! You two big boys! Run across to the town hall and bring us the big pot and the bowls we use for parties.

GASTON: We'll need water to fill the pot. Where can we get that?

MAYOR: Why, from this fountain right here in the square.

FIRST WOMAN: It's good, clear water, soldier. It's where we women come to get our water for cooking.

MAYOR: (*Smiling*) And where you hear the news of the village and talk about your neighbors!

GASTON: (*Politely*) Ah! Here come the boys with the big pot. Set it on the edge of the fountain, boys, so the water will go into it.

JEAN: While the pot is being filled, some of you will have to fetch some wood for a fire.

SECOND WOMAN: Of course! You can't make soup with cold water.

MAYOR: You children! Run and collect some wood.

STORYTELLER: Soon a big fire was burning by the fountain in the square. The big pot was set over it to boil. Then Gaston took the stone he had shown the people and dropped it into the pot.

GASTON: There! You all saw me drop the stone into the water. That's how I make the very best stone soup.

FIRST WOMAN: Good soup, with just some hot water and a stone? I don't believe it, soldier!

GASTON: Well, of course, any soup tastes better if you add some salt to the water, as you women know.

FIRST WOMAN: I'll have my little girl fetch some salt from my kitchen and some pepper, too.

JEAN: Thank you! Salt and pepper will improve the soup. Now, if we had some carrots, the soup would be even better. But what we can't have, we must do without.

SECOND WOMAN: Well — I have a few carrots at home. I–I think I can spare some. I'll send my little girl to get them. (*Aside*) Anna, you saw where we hid them. Run and bring as many as your apron will hold.

GASTON: Ah! Here's the child with the salt and pepper. I'll shake some into the water.

(*First Gaston sneezes, and then other people sneeze.*)

GASTON: Excuse me. It was the pepper. Bless you all! The water is boiling nicely, isn't it?

THIRD WOMAN: That still doesn't look like soup to me.

JEAN: Wait a little longer, my friend.

GASTON: Here come the carrots! Ah! The nice little girl has even washed them. Thank you, child. I'll slice them into the pot.

JEAN: The soup is beginning to look better already. Don't you agree? Of course, a good stone soup tastes even better with some cabbage and some potatoes added to the stone. But what we can't have, we must do without.

THIRD WOMAN: I'll send my boy back to my house for some potatoes and cabbage.

JEAN: Thank you, friend. (*A bit louder*) And would any of you good people suddenly remember that you had some meat at home that you could spare?

GASTON: Some meat would make this stone soup just perfect. It would make the soup

125

fit for the King himself. The King asked
for just this kind of soup the last time he ate
with us. Remember that, Jean?

JEAN: I remember that as perfectly as you do!

MAYOR: (*Wondering*) You soldiers have eaten
with the King? Really? And the King likes
this stone soup?

VOICES: They have eaten with the *King!*
Imagine that! The *King* likes stone soup!

STORYTELLER: Well, the farmers and the
villagers brought carrots and potatoes and
cabbage and meat to put into the water
along with Gaston's stone. The two
soldiers stirred the good thick soup while
the villagers stared in wonder.

GASTON: The soup is ready, friends. Take a
deep breath. Doesn't it smell wonderful?

FIRST WOMAN: (*Sniffs*) Mm! It certainly does!

SECOND WOMAN: And it was made with just a
small stone! Imagine!

JEAN: There's enough for all of us, I'm sure.
But now we need some benches and a long
table.

MAYOR: We have some we use at our village
fairs. Boys, fetch them from the Town Hall
cellar.

THIRD WOMAN: I think this soup would taste extra good if we had some fresh bread to eat with it. Let's each of us send to our home for a loaf of bread.

JEAN: Fine! The *King* likes bread with his soup, too.

GASTON: Yes, we'll eat like kings — and queens!

STORYTELLER: It was a wonderful party! The villagers agreed they had never tasted such fine soup. And how cheaply it could be made! All that was needed was a stone, with just a few things added. When they had finished eating, they pushed the tables and chairs to one side and stood talking and laughing among themselves.

GASTON: Why not end this party with some dancing? They always have dancing at the King's parties.

MAYOR: A fine idea, soldier! There's the Town Hall watchman with his violin. (*Calls*) Daniel! Give us some music! We'll end this party with some lively dancing!

STORYTELLER: At last everyone was tired, though happy.

GASTON: Will someone let us sleep in his hayloft?

MAYOR: What? Let two such fine men as you sleep in a hayloft? I should say not! One of you must sleep at my house. Who will take the other soldier?

VOICES: (*One at a time*) Come to my house! Come with us! I want him!

MAYOR: Good! Let's all say good night now.

VOICES: Good night! Good night!

STORYTELLER: The soldiers slept in soft beds that night. The next morning all the villagers gathered to say good-by to them.

MAYOR: We thank you, soldiers, for what you have done for us. Now that our women know how to make soup from a stone, we shall never go hungry.

GASTON: It's all in knowing how, your Honor.
   Good-by, friends!
JEAN: Good-by, my friends!
VOICES: Good-by! Good-by!

AUTHOR

Fan Kissen first worked as a teacher in the New York City schools. For many years she has written children's programs for a New York radio-TV station. One of these, *Tales from the Four Winds,* has been that station's most popular program for more than twenty years. Miss Kissen says, "The program is a series of folktales and legends from many different lands, showing how people round the world think and act in much the same way."

Fan Kissen has written a series of four books under the title *Tales from the Four Winds.* They are:

   The Bag of Fire and Other Plays
   The Crowded House and Other Plays
   The Golden Goose and Other Plays
   The Straw Ox and Other Plays

The play, "Stone Soup," was adapted by Fan Kissen from a story of the same name by Marcia Brown. Many of Miss Brown's best-known books are old folktales that she has retold in an interesting way. She also illustrates her own books. Two of them — *Cinderella* and *Once a Mouse* — have won the Caldecott medal for "best picture book of the year."

THE HUT

We built a hut, my brother and I,
Over a sandy pit,
With twigs that bowed and met above
And leaves to cover it.

And there we sat when all around
The rain came pouring down.
We knew if we were out in it
We'd both be sure to drown.

And though in puddles at our feet
Drops gathered from the sky,
We smiled through strands of dripping hair,
Because we felt so dry.

— HILDA VAN STOCKUM

131

**Skill
Lesson 3:**

GETTING MEANING FROM A DICTIONARY

When you are reading and meet a word for which
you have no meaning, you can often use the other
words in the sentence to find out what the word means.
But sometimes the other words won't give you enough
help. For example, read the following sentence to
yourself to see if you can get the meanings of the words
in heavy black letters:

Jim and his father got a **crate** for the **hutch**
they were going to build.

You should be able to say the two words that are in
heavy black letters, but you may not know what they
mean. In that sentence, the other words don't help you
figure out what those two words mean.

When the other words won't help you, you can use
a dictionary or a glossary. A **dictionary** is a book that

132

gives the meanings for many words and also tells you how to say those words. A **glossary** is something like a small dictionary. It is a list of words that sometimes appears at the back of a book to give help with words that are used in that book. You will find a glossary at the back of this book.

The words in a dictionary or glossary are shown in alphabetical order, like the names in a telephone directory. The words that begin with *a* come first, those that begin with *b* come next, and so on.

You can save time looking for words in a dictionary or glossary if you know how alphabetical order works. If the word you want begins with a letter that comes early in the alphabet, you should look for it near the beginning of the dictionary or glossary. If it begins with a letter near the middle of the alphabet, look for it near the middle. If it begins with one of the last letters in the alphabet, look for it near the end.

Suppose you wanted to find the word *trot* and the first word you saw when you opened the dictionary was *public*. Would you turn toward the front or the back of the dictionary to find the word *trot*? Since *t* comes after *p* in the alphabet, you should look for the word *trot* after the word *public*.

Now suppose you were looking for the word *rear* and saw the word *root*. Since both of these words begin with the same letter, you would have to use the alphabetical order of the second letter in the word to help you. The letter *e* comes before the letter *o* in alphabetical order, so you would look for the word *rear* before the word *root.*

Sometimes, the first *two* letters are the same in both the word you want and the one you see in the dictionary or glossary. If the first two letters are the same, use the alphabetical order of the third letters to decide whether to look ahead or back. Suppose you wanted to find the word *article.* Would it come before or after *arrive?* If the first three letters are the same, then use the alphabetical order of the fourth letters, and so on.

Just below is the top part of a page from the glossary at the back of this book:

---

prompt   **root**

prompt (prŏmpt) 1. Ready and   **range** (rānj) Open land where
    quick to act. 2. On time. 3. Re-   cattle graze.

Notice that there are two words in heavy black letters standing by themselves at the top of the page. Those words are called **guide words.** They are there to help you find the word you're looking for. The one at the left is the first word for which meanings are given on that page. The other is the last word for which meanings are given on that page. If the word you are looking for comes, in alphabetical order,

between those two words, look for it on that page. If it isn't there, it's not in the glossary at all. A dictionary works in exactly the same way.

Now let's see how well you can use alphabetical order and guide words to get the meaning of a word you don't know. Find the words *crate* and *hutch* in the glossary at the back of this book. Notice what each one means. Then read the sentence about Jim and his father again. This time you will know what they were going to do because you will know what those two words mean. When you don't know the meaning of a word you meet in this book, you will probably be able to get its meaning by looking it up in the glossary.

Discussion

Help your class answer these questions:

1. What is a crate? A hutch? What were Jim and his father going to do?

2. How does a dictionary help you with words?

3. What is a glossary?

4. How are the words listed in a dictionary or glossary?

5. How does knowing alphabetical order help you to use a dictionary or a glossary?

6. In a glossary, would the word *glide* come before or after the word *hutch?* Would the word *crate* come before or after the word *creek?* Use the glossary in this book to check your answers.

7. What are guide words in a dictionary or glossary? How can they help you? What are the guide words on the pages where *crate* and *hutch* are in this book's glossary?

8. Below are numbered rows of words, with three words in each row. Make believe that the first word in each row is one you are trying to find in a glossary or dictionary and that the other two words are the guide words on the first page you open to. Should you look for the word on that page, on an earlier page, or on a later page?

   1. **frantic**   glory — gulp

   2. **mesa**   linger — liquid

   3. **torch**   timid — urge

   4. **whimper**   traffic — zip

   5. **broil**   beaker — boom

   6. **label**   lantern — level

| 7. **calm** | calf — canyon |
| 8. **shrink** | shelter — shriek |

On your own

You may not know the meaning of some or all of the words in heavy black letters in the sentences below. Use the glossary at the back of this book to get the meaning of any you do not know.

Mary had always wanted to **possess** a horse. But the first night she had Candy, she left the barn door **ajar.** The next morning she saw that Candy was not in her **stall.** How **vexed** she was as she ran back to look for her! She found most of the **stock,** but Candy was nowhere to be seen.

Suddenly, Mary heard a loud **neigh.** It seemed to be coming from beyond some **briers.** That was where she found her **filly.** Candy had found a good place to **graze.** Mary was happy as she took hold of Candy's **mane** and led her back to the barn.

Checking your work

If you are asked to do so, give the meaning of one of the words in heavy black letters in the sentences about Mary and Candy. Then say the sentence in another way to show that you understand it.

SONG OF THE OPEN ROAD

I think that I shall never see
A billboard lovely as a tree.
Indeed, unless the billboards fall
I'll never see a tree at all.

– *Ogden Nash*

There are so many automobiles on the streets and roads today that it is hard to imagine a time when there were no cars. In the 1890's, most people were driving carriages pulled by horses.

At that time a few people had built automobiles, or "horseless carriages," as they were called. But it was a man named Henry Ford who made it possible for many people to have cars.

Henry Ford was born in Michigan in 1863. From the time he was a small boy, he loved to work with motors and engines. When he became a young man, he worked in Detroit in an engine shop. He began to see a few people driving around in "horseless carriages." He then decided to build his own in his spare time.

In 1896 Henry Ford finished his first car. It didn't look much like today's smooth, shiny

automobiles. It was shaped like a box and sat on four bicycle wheels. It had only one seat. This car had no steering wheel. Instead, it had a long, iron steering bar.

People would gather around and stare at Henry as he drove along the streets of Detroit. Horses, frightened by the strange chugging noises the car's engine made, would run away. The policemen were not too pleased with the up-roar this caused. Many people thought that automobiles were worthless and did not like them at all. Others would just laugh and shout to young Henry, "Get a horse!"

But Henry Ford did not give up. He was sure that the automobile would become an important part of people's lives. At that time, there were other cars being sold, but the cars were very expensive. Henry felt that everyone should be

able to own a car, not just the wealthy people. In 1903 he started the Ford Motor Company. His cars cost much less than other cars had before. By 1908 Henry Ford was selling a car known as the "Model T." This became the most popular car of its time.

Henry Ford's business was so successful that he was able to give jobs to more people and make more cars than anyone else. He was very good to the people who worked for him. He paid them well and also started a plan for all the workers to share in the money the company made. This worked so well that many other businesses began to do it, too.

The Henry Ford Museum is in Greenfield Village in Dearborn, Michigan. If you go there, you can see the first car that Henry Ford built in 1896. Believe it or not, that car still runs!

WHERE?

Where is that little pond I wish for?
Where are those little fish to fish for?

Where is my little rod for catching?
Where are the bites that I'll be scratching?

Where is my rusty reel for reeling?
Where is my trusty creel for creeling?

Where is the line for which I'm looking?
Where are those handy hooks for hooking?

Where is the worm I'll have to dig for?
Where are the boots that I'm too big for?

Where is there *any* boat for rowing?
Where is . . . ?

Well, anyway, it's snowing.

— *David McCord*

GOLDEN BOY

by
WILLIS LINDQUIST

Lanny Wilton bent low over his little white horse as it galloped across the valley. Although the three-mile race had just begun, Lanny was already far behind his friend Ted Ward.

Ted was riding his beautiful cream-colored palomino, and few horses could match her speed. Some day Lanny hoped to have a palomino, too.

Lanny's little white horse finally galloped into the canyon that marked the end of the race. Ted's palomino, Mesa (**may**-suh) Girl, was there, but Ted was nowhere in sight. Lanny walked up the slope and stopped in front of a thicket of greasewood.

"Come on out," he called. "I know you're in there!"

Ted grinned as he stepped from his hiding place. "How did you find me?"

"I heard the birds scolding you," Lanny explained. "Besides, you broke some branches off that greasewood. It gives off an oily smell."

Ted sniffed. "Honestly, Lanny, I never knew anyone like you! You know all about nature. And you can track like an Indian. How did you get that way?"

Starting down the slope, Lanny said, "Reading nature magazines, I guess. But when it comes to racing, you're the best."

"When you get a horse like Mesa Girl, it won't be so easy to beat you," Ted said. He whistled and his beautiful palomino came trotting up.

"I'll probably never get a palomino," Lanny said quietly. "Dad lost a lot of money on our ranch last year."

"My father did, too," said Ted. "All the ranchers lost money because of the dry season. Dad says times have been so bad he might have to sell Golden Boy. That's his best palomino."

"I'd like to see a horse half as good as your Mesa Girl," Lanny said.

"Well, come with me, then!" cried Ted. "It's about time you came over to our place anyway."

It was a five-mile ride, but Lanny didn't want to miss a

chance to see Golden Boy. Together they rode up to the corral.

The first sight of Golden Boy took Lanny's breath away.

"Oh, Ted! You can't sell a horse like that!" Lanny reached out slowly and rubbed the silky forehead. Golden Boy sniffed at him cautiously.

"Go easy," said Ted. "He's shy." With a snort, Golden Boy reared suddenly. Then he glided around the corral at an easy trot. Soon Golden Boy came back and put his head over the fence. Lanny edged closer and stroked his neck and mane.

Slowly Lanny climbed the corral fence, talking softly to Golden Boy all the while. He ran his hand through the silvery mane. Then he got a good grip and suddenly leaped onto the horse's back.

Golden Boy reared, but Lanny clung to the mane.

"Easy, boy, easy. Everything is all right." Lanny stroked the neck. He pressed his heels gently against Golden Boy's sides, and the horse calmed down. He began to trot around the corral.

Ted cried, "Lanny! I'm surprised you were able to get on him."

Lanny swung back to the corral fence and climbed off. Ted blinked in wonder.

Then they heard the slam of a door and turned to see Mr. Ward coming from the house. Ted said, "Dad, this is Lanny."

Mr. Ward smiled as he shook hands with Lanny. "Ted says you know a lot about nature. How do you like Golden Boy?"

"He was just riding Golden Boy bareback in the corral!" cried Ted.

"What?" Mr. Ward said in surprise. "You rode Golden Boy?"

"Show him, Lanny! Do it again!" said Ted.

Lanny did, and Golden Boy behaved perfectly. When Lanny came back, Mr. Ward said,

"Well, I'll be switched! That horse has taken a liking to you. Wait till my foreman hears this. He can't get near Golden Boy without a rope."

"Say, Dad," said Ted. "Why not let Lanny take him out to the range and ride him once in

a while? You said he needed training."

"Yes," said Mr. Ward, "and he also needs showing off, if I'm to sell him. Why don't you come back next Saturday and ride him again?"

When Lanny came home bursting with his good news, he found his father sitting before the fire in the living room.

"That's fine about Golden Boy," said his father, "but I'm afraid you'll have to forget about palominos, Lanny. We may have to move back to the city. I can't hold out much longer if this keeps up."

For a moment, Lanny was stunned. "If what keeps up, Dad?" he asked.

"The Forest Service man was out today with more orders," his father sighed. "They say we have too many cattle on the public range. The grass is being eaten out by the roots."

"What are we supposed to do about it?"

"We've got orders to sell off five hundred head of cattle by July first," Mr. Wilton answered. "If we do that, we won't have enough cattle left next year to keep the ranch going. We won't be able to pay our bills."

Strange Cargo

Things looked hopeless. But on Saturday, Lanny kept his promise to join Ted. When he arrived, Golden Boy was ready to ride.

"I don't wish your Dad any bad luck," Lanny said, "but I hope he won't be able to sell Golden Boy."

"He's got to," Ted said, "and we have to sell some cattle, too. We need the money badly, Dad says."

Lanny shook his head. It seemed as though everyone had to sell some cattle.

"I don't get it," he said. "Why should we have to sell our cattle when all that good grass is going to waste in the upper valley? Along those little creeks, the grass isn't half eaten."

"There's Mr. Nelson, the forest ranger," said Ted. "He's been out here talking with my Dad. Why not ask him?"

Lanny spoke to Mr. Nelson as he was leaving the house.

"Well," said Mr. Nelson, "by midsummer all those little creeks dry up."

Lanny thought for a moment. "But couldn't we dig some wells in the hills and keep the cattle up there on the good grass all summer?"

"Much too expensive," said Mr. Nelson.

There seemed to be no answer to the problem. Water was such a valuable thing when you didn't have it.

Then one day Lanny had an idea. With growing excitement, he looked through his nature magazines until he found the one he wanted. He took it to the Ranger Station.

"It might work," Mr. Nelson said, "if this article has the facts. Well, it won't do any harm to write and find out. We'll just have to wait and see."

For three weeks they waited and kept their secret. Then one day a green Forest Service truck arrived, carrying a very strange cargo.

Lanny knew he would never forget the day a couple of weeks later when the ranger came to speak to his father.

"Do you mean to say," Lanny's father said, "that I won't have to sell my cattle?"

"That's right," said Mr. Nelson. He gave Lanny a wink.

"But why this sudden change?" asked Mr. Wilton.

"Beavers! We've planted beavers in every one of the seventeen creeks on the upper ranges. They're building two or three dams on each creek already. The dams will hold back most of the water. We should

have water fifteen or twenty miles up on the range for the whole summer."

They heard the sound of a car. A moment later Mr. Ward and Ted came into the house. They were grinning.

"That certainly was a bright idea you had, Lanny," said Mr. Ward.

"What idea?" Mr. Wilton gave Lanny a puzzled glance.

"I haven't had a chance to tell him it was Lanny's idea," said the ranger. "Lanny came into my office several weeks ago with a magazine. An article in it said that beavers have become a real problem in some places. It said people were offering to trap them alive and ship them to wilder places where they might be useful. I was able to get a shipment of them free that way."

"Just in time, too," said Mr. Ward. "Lanny has saved every rancher around here thousands of dollars."

Lanny saw the proud look come into his father's face. "Yes," his father said to Lanny. "You've saved our ranch. I was about ready to give up."

"What I really came over here for," Mr. Ward said, "was to see if you might be interested in buying Golden Boy for Lanny."

Lanny caught his breath. He glanced at his father, who was shaking his head slowly. "I've been thinking of buying him a palomino, but — "

Lanny's heart sank. Nothing had changed after all.

"About price — " Mr. Ward was saying. "I'd make Lanny an even trade for the little horse he's been riding."

"Oh, no!" said Lanny's father. "I couldn't let you do that." He thought a moment. "But let's make it Lanny's horse and two hundred dollars."

Mr. Ward and Mr. Wilton shook hands on the deal.

Lanny was so surprised and happy that at first he couldn't speak. All he could think of to say was, "Oh, thank you!"

Then Lanny rushed out the door. A flash like honey in the sun had caught his eye. It was Golden Boy.

AUGHTHOR

AUTHOR

Willis Lindquist, author of "Golden Boy," loves nature just as Lanny did in the story. Mr. Lindquist enjoys taking nature pictures, and he has written about one trip into the mountains where he took pictures of beavers building their dam.

Mr. Lindquist also loves the sea and has sailed to many parts of the world. He once made a trip on a small sailing ship from Denmark to Australia. He has visited over forty different countries and has written some articles about them for *National Geographic* magazine.

Willis Lindquist has written about thirty books for boys and girls. You might enjoy such books as *Alaska: The 49th State*, *Burma Boy*, *Call of the White Fox*, and *Red Drum's Warning*.

FOAL

Come trotting up
Beside your mother,
Little skinny.
Lay your neck across
Her back, and whinny,
Little foal.
You think you're a horse
Because you can trot—
But you're not.
Your eyes are so wild,
And each leg is as tall
As a pole;
And you're only a skittish
Child, after all,
Little foal.

– Mary Britton Miller

STEVIE'S OTHER EYES

by Lois Eddy McDonnell

Stevie Sargeant sat on the back porch of his new home. Three steps led down to the backyard. In the yard there were things for Stevie to play with — a swing, a sandbox, a slide.

But today Stevie didn't want to swing or make a sand house or go down the slide. He sat on the top step, listening to the happy sounds next door.

Those sounds told him that Billy and Ed Green were playing ball. Ever since Stevie had moved to this house two weeks before, he had heard the boys playing next door. He wished they could be friends. His mother had told him that Billy was just his age. But Billy never spoke to Stevie, and neither did Ed, who was two years older. Stevie wondered if they would ever let him play with them.

Stevie stood up and walked slowly down the three steps and over to the fence. He put his hand on the rail and waited, hoping the boys would notice him. But they went on playing. They called to each other, shouted, and laughed. They did not seem to see Stevie.

Playing ball was fun, Stevie knew. Before he had moved to this new home, his father often played ball with him in the yard. He would bounce the ball and Stevie would listen to the sound and raise his hands. Father would throw the ball, saying, "Here it comes!" and Stevie would catch it.

At last Stevie called to Billy and Ed, "May I play ball with you?"

The sounds of playing grew still. No one said anything.

Then Billy spoke. "Aw, you can't play ball!" he said. "You're blind!"

"I can, too, play ball," Stevie said. "I've played it lots of times with my father."

"Then play with your father now," Ed called. A minute later, Stevie heard the thump of the ball again, as the boys threw it back and forth.

For a minute Stevie hung onto the fence hard. "Seeing isn't everything," he said, and turned away.

A long time ago Stevie's mother had told him that other people could see with their eyes. Well, Stevie had eyes. They told him when it was light or when it was dark, but they didn't tell him how things around him looked.

"But you have other eyes, Stevie," his mother had said. "You see with your fingers, and you have sharp ears to help you know what is happening."

Sometimes Stevie wished that his family still lived in Fairview. They had moved to the new home in Marshtown so that Stevie could go to a school that was just for blind boys and girls. His mother had told him about this special school called Brookside. She had said that he would stay at the school for five days every week. He would eat there and sleep there, but every weekend he would come home.

Stevie Learns to Read

Stevie did well that year at the Brookside School. He even learned to read. Blind people have a special way of learning to read. One weekend his teacher let him take one of the large books home.

When Billy saw Stevie and his big book, he called, "What do you have there?"

"It's my book," Stevie told him. "It tells all about boats. Come over and I'll read to you."

Billy followed him into the house.

The boys took off their jackets. Stevie sat down and opened the book.

Billy sat beside him. He looked with surprise at the book. "That's a funny book," he said. "There's not a picture in it. There's not a word either."

"Oh, yes, there is," Stevie said. "There are lots of words." He showed Billy the raised dots on the page. "Each of these dots helps to tell me a word."

"No kidding!" said Billy. "How do you know what they say?"

"I learned at school," Stevie replied.

"It's a funny kind of writing," Billy went on.

Mrs. Sargeant had been watching and listening. "I guess it does seem funny to you," she said to Billy. "This is a special kind of writing for blind people. It is called Braille (brale)."

"Braille!" said Billy. "That's a funny name."

"For many, many years blind people had no way to read," Mrs. Sargeant told him. "Then one day about a hundred years ago, a boy named Louis Braille had an accident that caused him to lose his sight. He went to a special school for boys and girls who were blind. When he grew up, he decided he would be a teacher of blind children. He tried to find better ways to teach them.

"Louis Braille knew that blind people could feel bumps that were made on smooth paper. He made up an alphabet of raised dots that could be read with the fingertips. Since then, other people have worked to make it easier to read raised dots. But this kind of writing is still called 'Braille' because Louis Braille invented it."

"Say, how do you like that!" Billy exclaimed. "Go ahead, read some of your book."

Stevie's fingers moved carefully across the page. He read, "Long ago, men had no boats. They could not ride in the water. They saw that

a log floats in water. Sometimes a man would hold on to a floating log and ride in the water.

"Then they found that they could hollow out a log and sit in it and ride in the water. This was the first boat ever used."

"That's interesting," Billy said. He looked at Stevie's book. "Where does it say 'boat'?" he asked.

Stevie pointed to the word. Billy's finger moved along the dots. "I don't know how you do it!" he said.

Somehow it seemed to Stevie that Billy was different after that day. Billy sometimes stopped to talk with him. One day he brought a model of a boat he had made.

That summer Stevie went to a camp just for blind boys. It was a wonderful vacation. Best of all, he learned how to swim and row a boat. Now the camp was over, and Stevie was coming home.

"My, how you've grown!" Mother said as she hugged Stevie. She and Father had come to meet him when he came back from camp.

Stevie was glad to be with his family again. It was only now that he knew how much he had missed them.

As they rode along in the car, Stevie had many things to tell. He did not remember going to sleep in the car, but when he woke up in the night, he was in his own bed. Everything was very still.

In the morning Stevie dressed and went downstairs.

"How is our sleepyhead?" Mother asked.

"I'm fine," Stevie said. "I'm hungry, too."

While he was eating breakfast, Mother told Stevie that, several days earlier, Billy Green had fallen from a tree he had been climbing. "It was a hard fall," she reported. "Billy had to go to the hospital for X-rays. His arm is broken in two places."

"Did Billy have to stay at the hospital?" Stevie asked.

"No," his mother replied. "His arm's in a cast now, and he's at home. His mother says it hurts."

"May I go visit him?" Stevie asked.

His mother agreed, and before long Stevie was feeling the heavy cast that covered Billy's arm.

"It's made of plaster," Billy explained. "So my arm can't move until the bones heal."

"How long will it have to stay on?" Stevie asked.

"I'll have to wear it the rest of the summer," Billy said unhappily. "I can't go swimming or ride my bike or play ball. I can't do anything — anything but sit."

Stevie didn't know what to suggest, but he told Billy about camp.

"I'd like to go to camp sometime," Billy said. "Maybe I can go there next year."

"I don't know about that," Stevie said. "You see, it's a camp for blind boys."

Billy looked surprised. "Do you mean that all the boys who go there are blind?"

"Yes," Stevie replied. "All of them are blind, although some can see a little."

After he went home, Stevie kept thinking about Billy, who seemed unhappy. Stevie wished he could think of something to make Billy feel better.

Another Way of Seeing

The next day Stevie met a friend of his, a man everybody called Daddy Thomas. Daddy Thomas had taken Stevie to the lake one day soon after the Sargeants had moved to town.

"How was camp?" he asked Stevie.

"Fine," Stevie replied. "I learned to row. I can really row a boat."

"I'm glad," Daddy Thomas said. "We must take another trip to Bubbling Lake soon. How about tomorrow afternoon?"

"I'll be ready," Stevie said.

That afternoon Stevie went back to visit Billy. Billy was cross. He couldn't find anything to do.

"This old cast is heavy," he complained. "I can hardly drag it around." Then he told Stevie that his brother Ed and some of his friends had written their names on it. "I wish you could write yours," Billy said.

Stevie had an idea. "I'll put an S in Braille on it — S for Stevie."

Mrs. Green brought a green crayon. Stevie carefully made the dots. It was not really like Braille, because it was not raised, but Billy was pleased. He wanted to go for a walk to show

others the latest name on his cast. Stevie walked
with him.

The next day it was hard for Stevie to wait
until afternoon. He kept thinking about the fun
he was going to have, and then suddenly he
remembered Billy. There were many things that
Billy couldn't do, now that his arm was broken,
but he could ride in a car. He could ride in a boat.
Stevie decided he would ask Daddy Thomas if
Billy might go with them to Bubbling Lake.

When Daddy Thomas's car stopped, Stevie hurried out.

"All aboard!" Daddy Thomas called.

"I want to ask you something first," Stevie told him. "Would you mind if another boy went along? Billy Green has a broken arm. There are a lot of things he can't do."

Of course Daddy Thomas said "Yes," and together they went to talk with Billy and his mother.

Before long, Daddy Thomas's car was moving along the highway. Two chattering boys sat beside him. They talked of many things, but mostly about boats.

"You'd better not stand up in the boat today," Stevie teased Billy. "If you tip it over, you and that big old cast will sink to the bottom of Bubbling Lake."

When they got to Bubbling Lake, Daddy Thomas took two fishing rods out of the car. "Maybe we'll get a nibble," he said. "Anyway, we'll take these along in the boat."

Daddy Thomas had arranged to use a friend's boat. He and Stevie dragged it to the water. They put the rods into the boat.

"What will be the best way for us to sit?" Daddy Thomas asked.

"If I sit in the middle seat, I can do the rowing," Stevie said. "You and Billy can sit in the back and tell me which way to go."

No sooner was it decided than they got in. Daddy Thomas wasn't sure if Stevie would have the strength to row them all. But he soon found there was no need to fear, for Stevie handled the boat well.

"You'll have to tell me when to turn," Stevie said.

"I'll do that," Billy said. "We'll soon be in the middle of the lake."

Stevie kept pulling on the oars.

"There's an island at the other end of the lake where we can fish," Daddy Thomas suggested.

"Then you must turn to your right," Billy said. Stevie pulled hard on the left oar. The boat moved down the middle of the lake. In a little while they were near the island.

"If you can make a landing here," Daddy Thomas said, "we can do our fishing."

Billy directed and Stevie followed. Soon the boat was on the beach. The boys got the fishing rods. They gave the longer one to Daddy Thomas.

Billy took the shorter rod. "I'll get the line ready," he offered. "I'll try to cast, but I can never hold it with this heavy thing on my arm. Will you hold the line, Stevie?"

Stevie agreed. He stood close to Daddy Thomas. Billy stood on the other side.

Standing quietly, Stevie held the rod and waited. By and by it seemed as if there was a nibble on his line.

Just then he heard Billy say, "Pull her in, Stevie. I think you've got a bite."

Stevie worked as fast as he could. As he turned the reel, he could feel a pull on the line. "I do have a bite!" he exclaimed.

"You have a fish!" Billy cried with delight, as Stevie pulled in his catch.

Together the boys took the fish off the hook. Stevie ran his hand along the fish. "Thirteen inches," he said.

Billy picked up Daddy Thomas's ruler. He measured the fish. "Thirteen inches," he said. "How did you know?"

"I can see with my hands," Stevie told him.

"I know you say that," Billy said, "but I can't do it."

"Oh, you could," Stevie said. "But you don't have to, because your eyes help you. I have another way of seeing."

"I never thought of that before," Billy said slowly. "You don't always need eyes to see."

"No," Stevie said. "But when I do need them, I just ask a friend to help."

The boys went on fishing, but no luck! After a while, Daddy Thomas told them it was time to go home. They put the rods back into the boat.

"Stevie, do you want me to row this time?" Daddy Thomas asked.

"Oh, no," Stevie replied. "I want to row the boat. If Billy will tell me which way to go, I'll take you back."

Stevie and Billy got into the boat. Daddy Thomas pushed the boat off the beach and got in, too. Stevie took the oars.

"You really can row, Stevie," Billy said. "You can row slick as a whistle."

"Thanks," Stevie said.

"Now turn to the right." Billy gave Stevie the command. "No fooling, Stevie," Billy went on, "we sure can do a lot of things together."

"We sure can," Stevie replied, pulling on the oars.

AUTHOR

This story is part of a book of the same title, *Stevie's Other Eyes,* by Lois Eddy McDonnell. You can find out more about Stevie by reading the rest of that book. You may be interested to know that the book has also been printed in Braille.

Lois Eddy McDonnell is a widow with two children, and she teaches at a college in Pennsylvania. She is familiar with many problems of blind people because her husband lost his sight.

Mrs. McDonnell has written another book about a child who must learn to live with a handicap. *Susan Comes Through the Fire* tells of a girl who has been very badly burned and the problems she faces. Mrs. McDonnell is also the author of *Hana's New Home.*

THE BRAILLE ALPHABET

A	B	C	D	E	F	G	H	I	J
K	L	M	N	O	P	Q	R	S	T
U	V	X	Y	Z	and	for	of	the	with
ch	gh	sh	th	wh	ed	er	ou	ow	W

SEEING EYE DOGS

For thousands of years, dogs have helped people in many ways. One of the most important jobs that dogs can do is guiding blind people.

In Morristown, New Jersey, there is a school where dogs are taught to do this special kind of work. The name of the school is "The Seeing Eye." At this school, special trainers spend about three months teaching each dog. The training must be done carefully because each dog will be responsible for the safety of someone who cannot see.

A Seeing Eye dog must learn to obey certain commands. But it must also learn to do things much harder for a dog to learn than that. It must learn to *refuse* to carry out a command that might cause harm to its owner. It will often have to decide whether to obey its master or not. That's why any Seeing Eye dog has to be a very smart one.

At the end of the training, the dog is tested to make sure it is ready to be fully responsible for a blind person. The dog's teacher is blindfolded, and he

"works" the dog at busy street corners and in heavy traffic.

When the dog has passed the test, the blind person who will be using the dog comes to stay at the school for a whole month.

He spends that time getting to know the dog and learning how to use it and take care of it.

How do the blind master and the dog work together? The master puts a short, U-shaped harness on the dog. He holds the handle of the harness tightly in his hand and learns to feel the dog's starts, stops, and turns.

The movements of the dog while it is in harness warn the master of anything dangerous that might be in his way, such as a hole in the sidewalk. The blind person learns how to direct his dog and how to understand the sign language that he feels through the harness handle. Day after day, the master and dog practice together on the streets of Morristown.

How does the dog know where its master wants to go? The blind person tells the dog. He knows his own city, and he can direct the dog by the commands, "Right," "Left," and "Forward." At street crossings, the dog guides its master to the edge of the curb and stops. The master finds the edge of the curb with his foot. Then, commanding the dog to go left, right, or forward, he goes on his way.

In a strange city, the master does just as the person who can see would do — he asks his way. Then he gives the directions in simple commands to his dog.

A blind person with a Seeing Eye dog does not have to depend on other people to take him where he wants to go. Besides this, he has a good and faithful friend with him at all times.

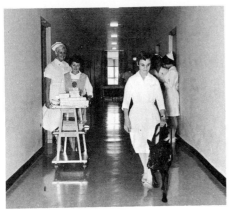

ELEPHANT WOOD

by Bill Severn

Have you ever wished you could do a magic trick and surprise your friends? Here is an easy one that you can do outdoors.

HOW IT LOOKS:

"This looks like a piece of Elephant Wood," you say, picking up a stick from the ground. "You know, some people say that elephants never forget, and I've heard that this wood has a good memory, too."

Never having heard of "Elephant Wood," your friends may be doubtful. You offer to show what you mean by having someone write his initials or the year of his birth. He is to scratch the letters or numbers in the dirt, or in the ashes from an old fire, with the end of the stick.

You tell him to rub out the initials with his shoe, so that no trace of them is left. Scooping some of the same earth with your hand, you rub it on your bare forearm. Then you tap your arm with the stick of Elephant Wood and show that it does have a magic memory. The same initials have appeared on your bare arm.

WHAT YOU NEED:

A bottle of rubber cement. This is a kind of transparent glue that comes with a brush.

HOW YOU FIX IT:

You decide ahead of time which of your friends you are going to ask to write with the stick. Wash your left forearm and dry it well. With the transparent rubber cement, paint his initials or the year of his birth on your arm. Use the brush that comes with the bottle, and make the letters as large as will fit. Let them dry. You can then forget about them until you are ready to perform.

WHAT YOU DO:

Choose a place where there is loose dirt or ashes and where there are a few small sticks lying around. Pick up one of them and talk about "Elephant Wood." Have your friend write his initials or birth year, whichever you have decided upon ahead of time. Then tell him to rub out the writing.

Scoop up some of the dirt and rub it on your arm. The writing will appear as the dirt clings to the rubber cement. But keep your arm toward yourself, and don't give away the surprise until you have tapped it with the magic "Elephant Wood."

This is one of many tricks described in Magic Wherever You Are *by Bill Severn. Other books about magic by Mr. Severn are* Magic in Your Pockets *and* Magic Shows You Can Give.

THe BuRninG OF THe RiCe FieLDS

by Lafcadio Hearn

Far away in Japan, many years ago, lived good old Hamaguchi (hah-mah-**goo**-chee). He was the wisest man of his village. and the people loved and honored him.

Hamaguchi was a rich farmer. His farmhouse stood on a hillside acre above the seashore. Down by the shore, and scattered up the hill, were the houses of his neighbors. Around his own house the ground was flat, like the top of a huge step in the hillside, and all about him stretched his rice fields.

It was the time of harvest. Hundreds of rice stacks dotted Hamaguchi's fields. There had been a fine crop, and tonight down in the village everyone was having a good time.

Hamaguchi sat outside his house and looked down into the village. He would have liked to join the merrymakers, but he was too tired — the day had been very hot. So he stayed at home with his little grandson, Tada (**tah**-dah). They could see the flags and the paper lanterns that hung, fluttering, across the streets of the village, and see the people gathering for the dance. The low sun lighted up all the moving bits of color.

It was still very hot, though a strong breeze

had begun to blow in from the sea. Suddenly the hillside shook — just a little, as if a wave were rolling slowly under it. The house crackled and rocked gently a moment. Then all became still again.

"An earthquake," thought Hamaguchi, "but not very near. The worst of it is probably far away."

Hamaguchi was not frightened, for he had felt the earth quake many a time before. Yet he looked anxiously toward the village. Then, suddenly, he rose to his feet and looked out at the sea. The sea was very dark, and, strange to say, it seemed to be running away from the land.

Soon all the village had noticed how the water was rolling out, and the people hurried down to the beach. Not one of them had ever seen such a thing before.

For a moment, on the hillside. Hamaguchi stood and looked. Then he called, "Tada! Quick — very quick! Light me a torch!"

Tada ran into the house, picked up one of the pine torches that stood ready for use on stormy nights, lighted it, and ran back to his grandfather. The old man grabbed the torch and hurried to the rice fields. Tada ran with him, wondering what he was going to do.

When they reached the first row of rice stacks, Hamaguchi ran along the row, touching the torch to each as he passed. The rice was dry, and the fire caught quickly, and the seabreeze, blowing stronger. drove the flames ahead. Row after row. the stacks caught fire. and soon flames and smoke towered up against the sky.

Tada ran after his grandfather, crying, "Grandfather, why? Why?"

Had his grandfather gone mad, that he was burning the rice that was their food and all their wealth? But Hamaguchi went on from stack to stack, till he reached the end of the field. Then he threw down his torch and waited.

The bell-ringer in the temple on the hill saw the flames and set the big bell booming. And, down on the beach, the people turned and began to climb the hill. If Hamaguchi's rice fields were afire, not the strangest sights of the shore should keep them from helping him.

First up the hill came some of the young men, who wanted to fight the fire at once. But Hamaguchi stood in front of the fields and held out his hands to stop them.

"Let it burn, lads," he commanded. "Let it burn."

The whole village was coming. Men and boys, women and girls, mothers with babies on their backs, and even little children came. Children could help pass buckets of water. Even the old men and women came very slowly, as best they could.

Still Hamaguchi stood in front of his burning fields and waited. Meanwhile the sun went down.

The people began to question Tada. What had happened? Why wouldn't his grandfather let them fight the fire? Was he mad?

"I don't know," sobbed Tada, for he was really frightened. "Grandfather set fire to the rice on purpose. I saw him do it!"

"Yes," cried Hamaguchi. "I set fire to the rice. Are all the people here?"

The men of the village looked about them and

answered, "All are here, but we cannot understand —"

"Look!" shouted Hamaguchi, as loud as he
could, pointing to the sea. "Look! Now do you
think I've gone mad?"

All turned and looked through the dim light,
over the sea. Far, far out, where sea and sky
seemed to meet, stretched a cloudy line that
came nearer and nearer, and broadened out larger
and larger. It was the sea coming back to the
shore. It towered like a great wall of rock. It
rolled more swiftly than a kite could fly.

"The sea!" shrieked the people. Hardly had
they spoken, when the great waters struck the
shore. The noise was louder than any thunder.
The hillside shook. A sheet of foam was dashed
up to where the people stood. When the sea went
back, not a house was left below them on the

hillside or along the shore. The village had been swept away.

The people stood silent, too frightened to speak, until they heard Hamaguchi saying gently, "That was why I set fire to the rice. . . . My house still stands, and there is room for many. The temple on the hill still stands. There is shelter there for the rest."

Then the people woke, as if from a dream, and understood. Hamaguchi had made himself poor to save them, and they bowed their foreheads to the ground before him.

AUTHOR

Lafcadio Hearn was born in 1850 on the Greek island of Santa Maura. His mother was Greek, and his father was a doctor in the British army. He was soon taken to England where he spent his boyhood. During this time, he lost the sight of one eye in an accident. But this did not keep young Lafcadio Hearn from his love of reading and writing. He came to the United States and wrote interesting and unusual articles for newspapers. He then went to Japan to teach English in Japanese schools. He got married there and in time became a Japanese citizen. Many of his stories are about Japan.

Mr. Hearn died in 1904, but some of his writings are still in print. You might enjoy *The Boy Who Drew Cats and Other Tales* and *Japanese Fairy Tales*.

What's wrong with this picture?

190

**Skill
Lesson 4:**

CHOOSING THE RIGHT MEANING

Look at the words in heavy black type below:

1. See the **duck** out on the pond.

2. Did you see him **duck** out of the way?

3. I'll **change** into my work clothes now.

4. How much **change** did you get back?

You can see that the word *duck* has a very different meaning in Sentence 2 from the meaning it has in Sentence 1. In Sentences 3 and 4, the word *change* is used with two very different meanings. There are many words with more than just one meaning.

A dictionary usually shows all the meanings a word may have, or at least its most common meanings. A glossary usually gives only the meanings the word has in the book in which you find the glossary, or it may give all the common meanings of the word.

191

Suppose you meet a word that you have to look up in a dictionary and you find more than one meaning given for that word. How can you know which meaning to use?

Once again, the context in which you first met the word will help you. As you read each meaning that is given for such a word, decide whether or not that meaning would make sense in the sentence in which you found the word. Then choose the meaning that makes the best sense in that sentence.

For example, suppose you came to this sentence in your reading and you didn't know the meaning of the word in heavy black letters:

She was wearing a **mulberry** dress.

If you looked the word up in a dictionary, here is what you might find:

mulberry. 1. A kind of tree. 2. The fruit of a mulberry tree. 3. Reddish purple, the color of a ripe mulberry.

You would know at once that meanings 1 and 2 were not right, because you wouldn't expect a girl's dress to be made of a tree or of some kind of fruit. You would decide that meaning 3 must be the right one here because the meaning "reddish purple" would make good sense in that sentence.

Discussion

Help your class answer these questions:

1. Which is more likely to give more meanings of a word, a dictionary or a glossary? Why?

2. There are many common words for which you already know at least two meanings. What meanings do you know for each of the following words?

trip	**light**	**block**	**letter**	**watch**
loaf	**stamp**	**jam**	**spoke**	**park**

3. When you find more than one meaning for a word in a dictionary or glossary, what should you do to help you decide which meaning you should use?

4. What meaning that the glossary at the back of this book gives is the right one for each of the words in heavy black letters in the following sentences?

   1. We could hear someone **prompt** the actor.
   2. He placed his **level** along the edge of the roof.
   3. The dime bounced and fell through the **grating.**
   4. There was a jerk as he let in the **clutch.**
   5. Every time I ask him a question, he **hedges.**

On your own

Each of the words in heavy black letters in the numbered sentences below has more than one meaning.

Use the glossary at the back of this book to decide on a correct meaning for each one, if you don't already know that meaning. Then rewrite each sentence so that it says the same thing without using the word in heavy black letters.

1. He had a big black-and-blue mark on his **calf.**
2. Mother will **stuff** the chicken and then roast it.
3. Only a fool would **crow** about having done that simple little trick.
4. No one in his **circle** of friends had been able to do the problem.
5. One of the strings in his **racket** was broken.
6. We laughed as we watched the kitten **stalk** a fallen leaf.
7. She spooned the **batter** into a baking pan.
8. It's a cup that **telescopes** to save space.
9. Two of the men on the **force** were able to **force** the door.
10. You'd better take this **cape** if you're going over to the **cape** in this fog.

Checking your work

If you are asked to do so, read one of the sentences above and then the new sentence you wrote for it. Find out if others agree that you chose the right meaning.

SOMETIMES

Sometimes I share things,
And everyone says,
"Isn't it lovely? Isn't it fine?"
I give my little brother
Half my ice-cream cone
And let him play
With toys that are mine.

But today
I don't feel like sharing.
Today
I want to be let alone.
Today
I don't want to give my little brother
A single thing except
A shove.

– Eve Merriam

MAGIC IN A GLASS JAR

by

RHODA BACMEISTER

One Saturday, Uki Sakaya (**oo**-kee sah-**kah**-yah) took his little sister Shuzuko (shoo-**zoo**-ko) for a walk. They walked around the paths of the big housing project where they lived with their parents and their grandmother. They knew they mustn't walk on the fresh, green grass of the lawns. But they could hunt under the hedges along the walks for beetles, ants, or earthworms.

They found some ants trying to carry away a dead beetle much bigger than themselves. It was fun to watch them tug and pull. Then Uki saw a still more surprising thing. There on a weed was a big, fat, green caterpillar. It had red, yellow, and blue spots all along the sides of its body.

"Oh, Shuzuko, look!" he cried. "Let's find a can or box and take him home."

Shuzuko looked around and came back with an empty popcorn box. Uki started to pick up the caterpillar. But the caterpillar held onto the plant with all his feet and wouldn't let go. The

only thing to do was to pick the branch he was on and put him, branch and all, into the box. At first the caterpillar stopped eating, but soon Uki and Shuzuko saw him begin again. They thought it very strange to see him open his mouth sideways instead of up and down.

On their way back to the apartment they met Jack in the elevator. "What have you got in the box, Jimmy?" he asked.

Uki wasn't surprised to be called Jimmy. Like most Japanese children in America, he had two different first names, Uki for home, and Jimmy for outside. Shuzuko's American name was Suzy.

They showed Jack the caterpillar.

"Boy! I bet your mother won't let you keep him!" Jack said.

Uki wasn't sure she would, either. When they got home, he went straight to his room and left the box there. Mother Sakaya was putting the rice and vegetables on the table for lunch. The children sat down without speaking of the caterpillar.

But after a while Shuzuko wanted to tell. "We found a pretty worm," she said.

Mother jumped. "A worm! Where?"

Uki saw he couldn't keep it a secret. "Under a bush. Wait a minute and I'll show you." Off he ran and brought back the box with the caterpillar. "See, he's got red and yellow spots!"

But Mrs. Sakaya didn't like caterpillars. She wrinkled up her nose. "Ugh!" she said. "I don't want any worms in this house — dirty, crawly things! You'd better put it right back outside."

Uki and Shuzuko looked at each other. Shuzuko's eyes began to fill with tears. But not Uki's. He hung his head but he said, "No, he isn't dirty. He's pretty."

All this time, the grandmother had been sitting at the table. She was pouring a little tea into her rice and eating it with a pickle, as she liked to do. Now she looked at the caterpillar. "Let me see," she said quietly.

"Isn't he pretty, Oba-ah San (**oh**-bah **sahn**)?" Uki asked. He used the polite Japanese word for *grandma*, which he knew she liked.

"He is very pretty," she said. Then she turned to Uki's mother. "A caterpillar is not a dirty animal. I remember when I was a girl how some people raised caterpillars on mulberry leaves.

Those were silkworms, of course. They made lovely little cream-colored cocoons that we sold to make silk."

That settled it. Uki could keep his caterpillar. No one would think of disagreeing with Oba-ah San, the oldest of the family. She even told the children how to make a better home for their new pet. They put a little earth in the bottom of a big glass jar. Then they put the caterpillar and the leaves he was eating into that. They tied a cloth over the top so that he couldn't get out but air could get in. Oba-ah San sent them out to get more leaves. Afterward, they always brought him fresh leaves once or twice a day. They named their pet Keizo (**kay**-zo).

Keizo ate and ate and grew bigger and bigger. He must have eaten all the time, because each morning the leaves would be gone. The children loved to watch his mouth opening and shutting sideways in the middle of his face. If they were very quiet, sometimes they could even hear him crunch the leaves. "Doesn't he ever sleep?" they wondered.

One morning the leaves were not eaten. There at the bottom of the jar lay Keizo.

"*Now* he's gone to sleep," Shuzuko said.

Uki wasn't so sure. But he thought they had better let him rest, so they went out to play. When they came back, Keizo looked stranger than ever. He was moving a little, as if he wanted to pull a dry leaf closer. There was some fuzzy white stuff across part of his body.

"Keizo looks sick," Uki cried and ran to get Oba-ah San.

"Is he going to die?" Uki asked her.

Oba-ah San laughed, covering her mouth with her hand for politeness. "No, Uki-bo, he is all right," she said, using her pet name for Uki. "He is only changing as all caterpillars do when they are ready. He will make a cocoon and sleep in it for a few weeks. When he comes out, he will be a moth with big wings, and he will be able to fly."

This seemed almost too wonderful to believe, but that was what Oba-ah San said. They watched while their caterpillar slowly made himself a loose cocoon inside the leaves. Then he lay still and did not move inside his cocoon.

The next day and the next they looked at him, but he was just the same. They more or less forgot about him for a while. Then one day a few weeks later, Uki happened to look into the jar. He called Shuzuko. "Oh, come and see! Keizo did come out! He isn't a caterpillar any more. But he didn't grow big wings. He has only little crumply bunches."

They called Oba-ah San, and she told them to wait. The wings would open. Very slowly they did. The children looked every few minutes as they played about the house. Every time, the wings had stretched out bigger. In a couple of hours they were open wide.

There was their old friend Keizo, the green, spotted caterpillar. He was changed into a big, soft, tan moth with wings so wide they almost touched the sides of the jar. His body had brown and yellow markings. Each of his wings had a

large spot. Uki, Shuzuko, and Oba-ah San all thought he was beautiful.

"Let's show Mama," Uki said.

When she saw him, Mrs. Sakaya agreed. "Yes, he really is lovely now. I am glad you kept him. But what now? Will he still eat leaves?"

"I don't think moths ever do," Oba-ah San said. "I guess we will have to let him go when evening comes and it is time for moths to fly. Then he will find whatever food he needs."

Uki and Shuzuko looked sad. But they could see that they would not be able to keep Keizo in the future. Keizo would have no room to fly in the jar, and the children wouldn't know what to feed him.

They watched Keizo resting quietly all day. As it grew dark, he began to stir and flutter. It was time to let him go. They took the jar out where they had first found Keizo and gently tumbled him onto a bush.

Keizo caught hold of a leaf with his six slim legs. He balanced himself for a moment and then softly fluttered up. They all watched him go.

"Good-by, Keizo! Have a happy time!" they called.

AUTHOR

"Magic in a Glass Jar" is one of the stories from the book, *The People Downstairs,* by Rhoda Bacmeister. Mrs. Bacmeister likes to write about children of all races and national backgrounds. She herself lives in a housing development in New York City.

Mrs. Bacmeister was born Rhoda Warner in Northampton, Massachusetts, and was a teacher for many years. In 1917 she married Otto Bacmeister, and they had three children. She is now very proud of being a great-grandmother.

Now retired and a widow, Mrs. Bacmeister has such interesting hobbies as weaving her own cloth. She is also the author of *Voices in the Night,* a book about the underground railroad during the Civil War.

THE TICKLE RHYME

"Who's that tickling my back?" said the wall.
"Me," said a small
Caterpillar. "I'm learning
To crawl."

– *Ian Serraillier*

ONLY MY OPINION

Is a caterpillar ticklish?
    Well, it's always my belief
That he giggles, as he wiggles
    Across a hairy leaf.

– *Monica Shannon*

FEET

Feet of snails
are only one.
Birds grow two
to hop and run.
Dogs and cats
and cows grow four.
Ants and beetles
add two more.
Spiders run around
on eight,
which may seem
a lot, but wait —
Centipedes
have more than thirty
feet to wash
when they get dirty.

— Aileen Fisher

207

MORE BOOKS TO ENJOY

BLAZE AND THE LOST QUARRY, *by Clarence W. Anderson.*
This is one in a popular series of books about Billy and his horse Blaze.

LAND OF SILENCE, *by Anna Rose Wright.*
A boy hates school until he begins to work with a special class of deaf children.

LENTIL, *by Robert McCloskey.*
Lentil can't sing, but he plays a very remarkable harmonica.

MISTER PENNY'S RACE HORSE, *by Marie Hall Ets.*
A farmer takes his animals to the fair in this very funny story.

ONCE A MOUSE, *by Marcia Brown.*
This is an old folktale from India in which a hermit thinks about "big" and "little" as he uses his magic charms.

SALT BOY, *by Mary Perrine.*
A young Indian boy's quick thinking saves one of his father's sheep.

SUMI'S SPECIAL HAPPENING, *by Yoshiko Uchida.*
A Japanese girl looks for a very special present for the oldest man in the village.

REALMS

REALMS

EDDIE and the DOLL

by Carolyn Haywood

Eddie Wilson was all excited. It was the town's yearly Clean-up Week. This was the week when people gathered together the things they no longer wanted. These things were then sold to help swell the United Fund. The sale was always held in a big empty store on Main Street.

Each year Eddie went to the sale with the money he had saved. He had gotten lots of his valuable property this way. Eddie's family would call it "junk," but that did not matter to Eddie. There had been times when even his father had been forced to admit that Eddie had brought home "some swell stuff." Now Eddie was hoping to find a doll that his friend Anna Patricia would like. He wanted to trade it for an old printing press that she had.

On Monday afternoon, on his way home from school, Eddie stopped in at the store. There were piles of things heaped on the floor, and several women were sorting them over. Eddie looked around. Then one of the women said,

"Run along, little boy. The sale is tomorrow. Run along now. You're in the way."

Eddie moved toward the door. Just before he went out, he passed a pile of broken toys. Sitting on top of the lot was a battered old doll. She was a big doll, and she looked as though someone had treated her quite badly. She had lost her wig, and a big hole showed in the top of her head. But, in spite of the dirt on her face, Eddie could see that she was pretty. She was wearing a faded, wrinkled blue dress. Even in her battered state, she made Eddie think of Anna Patricia.

Suddenly he had an idea. He ran back to the woman who had spoken to him and said, "Couldn't I just buy that doll over there? Couldn't I?"

The woman stopped her work and looked over to where Eddie was pointing. "Well, now," she said. "Aren't you a sweet brother to think of a doll for your sister!" She turned to her helpers. "Shall we let this little boy have that doll?"

"Oh, yes, let him have it," said the others.

"How much is it?" Eddie asked.

"I guess ten cents is about right," said the

woman. Eddie dug into his pocket and pulled out ten cents. "Take it along," said the woman.

"Well . . . well, could you wrap it up?" said Eddie.

"Oh, no!" she replied. "We haven't any wrapping paper yet."

"Okay," said Eddie, but he had a worried frown on his face as he picked up the big doll.

Before he left, he peeked out the door. He looked up and down the street. There was no one in sight, so he went outside. He decided to keep to the back way, so he dashed around the corner and ducked into a narrow street.

Right away he knew that he had made a mistake, for there were two boys playing ball in the street. Eddie ran back quickly to Main Street. There he found three boys coming toward him. Eddie put the doll on a step in a doorway and walked on. When the three boys passed him, Eddie was looking in a store window. He made believe that he was very much interested in something in the window.

He made believe so well that he did not see a big dog come around the corner. The dog went right up to the doll, and in a moment he had taken it in his mouth and was running away with it.

When the boys were out of sight, Eddie went

back for the doll. He was surprised to find that it was gone. Then he thought perhaps he had forgotten where he had left it, so he looked in other doorways. When he failed to find the doll, he went on his way, feeling very puzzled.

He had gone about two blocks when he saw, lying on the sidewalk of the next block, something that looked like the doll. He began to run. When he had gone about half the distance, he saw a man pick up the doll. The man looked at the doll. Then he looked around. Eddie saw him put the doll in a baby carriage that was parked on the sidewalk. The man walked on.

When Eddie reached the baby carriage, he found that it was standing right beside the door of a grocery store. A baby was sitting in the carriage and had just taken a firm clutch on the doll's dress. Eddie reached in and took hold of the doll. The baby screamed. Eddie tugged. The baby screamed louder.

The door of the grocery store opened. Out came a woman with a big bundle in her arms. She looked at Eddie and the baby and said to Eddie, "Aren't you ashamed of yourself! A great big boy like you, tormenting that little baby! Take your hands off that doll."

"But it's mine," said Eddie.

"Oh, so it's yours!" said the woman with the bundle. "So you play with dolls, do you?" She went on her way.

Just then the door opened again, and another woman came out. She looked at the doll in the carriage. Her eyes grew very big. She grabbed the doll away from the baby and looked at Eddie.

"What do you mean by putting that filthy, dirty doll in my baby's carriage?" she shouted. She pushed the doll into Eddie's arms and angrily wheeled the screaming baby away.

Eddie stood holding the doll. "If only I could get a paper bag!" he thought. He looked through the door of the grocery store. There were several people inside, but he just had to have a paper bag. Eddie held the doll behind his back and went in.

"What do you want, son?" said a man who was leaning over a basket of potatoes.

"Would you please give me a paper bag?" said Eddie.

"Help yourself," said the man. "I'm busy."

Eddie backed into a basket of apples and dropped the doll on top of the apples. Then he bent down and began looking through the paper bags. There were many sizes, but none large enough. "Where in the world are the big ones?" thought Eddie frantically.

He was still looking through the paper bags when he heard a man's voice say, "Who left this doll baby in the apple basket?" Eddie looked around, and there stood one of the clerks with the doll in his hand. He was holding it up, and everyone in the store had turned to look at him.

Eddie could feel his face burning. He went on looking for a paper bag. Then he heard the man's voice again. "Somebody is always leaving something around here. Doll babies in the apples! Yesterday it was a wooden soldier in the onions." Then he called out, "Bill, if any-body comes back for this, it's right up here on this shelf."

The Super Doll

Just then Eddie came upon a big paper bag. He straightened up and looked around. There sat the doll on the very top shelf.

"Did you get your bag, son?" said the first man.

"Yes, I found one," said Eddie. "Thanks."

"Well, so long!" said the man.

Eddie lingered. In a few minutes the man said, "What else do you want?"

Eddie looked along the shelves. "I . . . I . . . I'm just looking," he said.

"Can't you remember what your mother told you to get?" said the man.

Eddie gulped. "Uh," he said. "Uh — do you have any pickles?"

"Sure!" said the man. "How many do you want?"

"Just one," said Eddie.

The grocery clerk put a pickle into a bag and handed it to Eddie. "A nickel," he said.

Eddie handed over a nickel and went outside. He lingered on the sidewalk by the door and ate the pickle. He watched the shoppers go in and out the door. The store was not empty for a single moment. He had almost finished the pickle when he noticed that there was no one in the store. Eddie darted in.

"You back again?" said the grocer. "Forget something?"

At that moment the door opened, and in came two big boys who were friends of Eddie's brother Rudy. "Hi, Eddie!" they shouted.

The grocer was looking down at Eddie. "Hurry up, son. What do you want?" he said.

Eddie hesitated. Then he said, "Uh — do you have any sweet rolls?"

"No sweet rolls," said the man.

"Well . . . uh . . . I guess I'll take an apple."

The man picked an apple out of the basket and handed it to Eddie. "Three cents," he said. Eddie handed over three cents and left the store. Again he stood outside. He ate the apple. He hoped he was not going to have to spend any more of his money. First it had been the doll, then the pickle, and now the apple. He had spent almost a quarter.

In and out, in and out the door went the shoppers. At last the store was empty again. Eddie tore in like a ball of fire. "Please, mister!" he cried, pointing up at the doll. "That's mine. Can I have it quick, mister?"

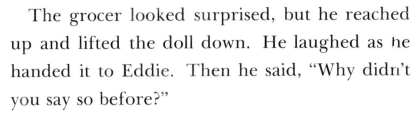

The grocer looked surprised, but he reached up and lifted the doll down. He laughed as he handed it to Eddie. Then he said, "Why didn't you say so before?"

Eddie stuffed the doll into the big paper bag. "I couldn't," he said. "I'm not going to keep it. It's for somebody else. I hate it."

Eddie had never been so glad to open his own front door. He ran right down to the basement. Now he would see what could be done with this doll. He knew it would need a lot of fixing before he could offer it to Anna Patricia in exchange for the printing press. It would have to look pretty super. First thing, he thought, was to see if he could get it clean.

He took the doll out of the paper bag and put it into the washtub. He poured in some soap and

turned on the water. The running water made so much noise that he did not hear his brothers, Joe and Frank, come down the basement stairs. They were right behind him before he knew that they were there.

They looked over Eddie's shoulder. When they saw the big doll sitting in the tub, they both screamed. "Why, Eddie!" cried Joe. "Aren't you the cute little thing! Where did you get that sweet little dolly?"

"Eddie!" cried Frank. "What a dear little snookie-ookums!"

There was a piece of hose fastened to the water faucet. Eddie reached for the hose, turned on the water full force, put his finger across the end of the hose, and sprayed it in the direction of his brothers. The boys ran from the shower bath.

Mrs. Wilson came down to see what the racket was about.

"Mother!" cried Joe. "Your youngest son has a doll baby."

"Mom!" Eddie cried. "Please come help me. I don't know what to do with this thing."

Mrs. Wilson went over to Eddie. "Look, Mom," he said. "I'd like to have a printing press like the one Anna Patricia has. She never uses hers, and she likes to collect dolls. Maybe if I could make this doll look nice, she'd trade me the printing press for the doll."

Mrs. Wilson picked up the dripping doll.

"Well, Eddie," she said. "This doll will need a lot of fixing, I'm afraid, before Anna Patricia would even look at it."

"Do you think you could do anything with it, Mom?" he asked.

Mrs. Wilson looked at the doll. "It needs everything," she said. "First of all, it needs a wig."

Eddie's face lighted up. "Oh, I know where I can get a wig," he said. "I have an old one here somewhere."

"I'll be up in the sewing room," his mother said.

A little while later, Eddie appeared at the sewing-room door. He held up the wig. "Found it!" he cried.

"That's good," said his mother. "Now we can finish this doll."

Mrs. Wilson took the wig out of Eddie's hand and began to cut and shape a piece of it to fit the doll's head. Eddie went out to put some air into his bicycle tires.

When he returned, his mother called to him. "Eddie," she said. "Come see if you think Anna Patricia would like this doll, now that it's finished."

Eddie went into the sewing room. He looked at the doll. He couldn't believe it was the same doll he had bought for ten cents. This doll looked like a princess with golden curls. His mother had dressed it in some thin, white stuff and had sewed something all over it that looked like diamonds. There was a blue velvet coat, and even little red shoes.

"Oh, Mom!" said Eddie. "I don't know much about dolls, but that sure looks super to me."

"I have a box you can put it in," said his mother.

"I'll take it over to Annie Pat's right now," said Eddie.

"I'll drive you over," said his mother. "You can't manage the box on your bicycle."

"Oh, that's swell of you, Mom," said Eddie.

When they reached Anna Patricia's house, Eddie rang the doorbell, and Anna Patricia came to the door. "Hello, Eddie!" she said. "What have you got there?"

"Oh, Annie Pat! I have something for you," said Eddie. "Just wait till you see it!"

"For me?" said Anna Patricia.

Eddie put the box down and began to untie the string. "You remember, Annie Pat?" he said.

"You said if I ever found a doll for you, you'd give me the printing press."

"Well," said Anna Patricia, sounding a little uncertain. "You know I said maybe. I didn't say for sure."

But then Eddie lifted the lid, and Anna Patricia had her first look at the doll. "Oh!" she said. "Oh! She's beautiful!"

Eddie sighed with relief. "Do you like it, Annie Pat?"

"Oh, yes!" she replied. "You can have the printing press, Eddie."

"Yippee! Yippee!" yelled Eddie.

Anna Patricia's father came into the room. "What's all the racket?" he asked.

"Annie Pat gave me the printing press!" Eddie shouted. "She gave me the printing press!"

"That's great!" said her father. "That thing's been in the way long enough. I see your mother's outside in your car. I'll help you put the printing press into the trunk of the car."

"Oh, thanks!" said Eddie.

Eddie and Anna Patricia's father carried the printing press out of the garage and placed it very carefully in the trunk of the car.

Eddie was beaming as he rode home beside his mother. "Now I can print all I want, Mom," he said. "I can print a newspaper and cards and all kinds of things. I can make money, Mom!" He looked up at his mother and grinned. "And do you know what?"

"What?" said his mother.

"I'm going to buy you a present," said Eddie.

THE END

AUTHOR

Boys and girls have enjoyed Carolyn Haywood's stories about Eddie for many years. This story is from one of her books in the "Eddie" series, *Eddie and His Big Deals.* Some of the other books about Eddie and his friends are *Little Eddie, Eddie and Louella,* and *Ever-Ready Eddie.*

Carolyn Haywood was born in Philadelphia, Pennsylvania. She is not only a well-known writer but also a portrait painter. She especially likes to do portraits of children. Her first book, *"B" Is for Betsy,* was an instant success and was the start of another popular series. Some other "Betsy" books by Carolyn Haywood are *Betsy and the Boys, Snowbound With Betsy,* and *Betsy and Mr. Kilpatrick.* Other books of Miss Haywood's that you might also enjoy are *Here Comes the Bus!* and *Robert Rows the River.*

A Joke

Mother:	Milton! What was that crash?
Milton:	Mom, do you remember that glass bowl you were always worried about, because you were afraid I'd break it?
Mother:	Yes. What about it?
Milton:	Well, your worries are over!

GETTING PRONUNCIATIONS FROM A DICTIONARY

Do you know the meaning of each of the two words printed in heavy black letters in the following sentences?

1. Now that fall had come, John's father was going to **stow** his boat under the porch.
2. Mary asked Dick to help her build a tree house, but he said he didn't want to **wield** a hammer all day.

You know how to use a dictionary or glossary to get the meaning of a word that you meet in your reading and do not know. If you did that now, you would find that in the first sentence the word *stow* means "put away" or "arrange in place." In the second sentence, the word *wield* means "hold and use as a tool."

Suppose now that you needed to read the two sentences aloud or wanted to use the words *stow* and *wield* in talking with someone. Which would you make the word *stow* rhyme with: *cow* or *know?* Which would you make *wield* rhyme with: *field, child,* or *held?*

Whenever you read to or talk with other people, you should **pronounce** each word correctly. If you don't do this, people who are listening may have trouble figuring out just what you are saying.

What can you do to find out all by yourself how to pronounce a word you're not sure about? You can use a dictionary or glossary.

Here is the way the words *stow* and *wield* appear in the glossary at the back of this book:

stow (stō)   1. Put away.   2. Arrange in place.
wield (wēld) Hold and use as a tool.

Notice what comes between the word itself and its meaning or meanings. That is called a **special spelling.** It is put there to show you the correct pronunciation of the word. To figure out what that pronunciation is, you have to use what is called a **pronunciation key.** That key appears at the bottom of every page or every other page in a dictionary or glossary. Here is the one that is used in this book's glossary:

ă pat / ā pay / âr care / ä father / ĕ pet / ē be / ĭ pit / ī pie / îr fierce / ŏ pot / ō toe / ô paw, for / oi noise / ou out / oͦo took / o͞o boot / th thin / *th* this / ŭ cut / ûr turn / yo͞o use / ə about / zh pleasure

Look at the special spelling for *stow*. The letters *s* and *t* there tell you that the sounds for those two letters are just what you would expect them to be. Notice that the other letter in the special spelling is an *o* with a straight line above it. Now find an *o* with a straight line above it in the pronunciation key. You can see the word *toe* coming right after it, with *oe* in heavy black letters. That word *toe* is called a key word. It tells you that *o* in a special spelling stands for the vowel sound you hear in the word *toe*. Since *o* is the last letter in the special spelling for *stow,* the letters *ow* in *stow* stand for the sound you hear at the end of *toe*. Now you know that you should pronounce *stow* so that it rhymes with *toe* and *know*.

Now let's do the same thing with the special spelling for *wield*. Look at the mark over the *e* in that special spelling. Now find an *e* with that mark over it in the pronunciation key. What key word comes right after that ē? Say that key word to yourself and listen for its vowel sound. Then think that same vowel sound for the ē in the special spelling for *wield*. Which does *wield* rhyme with: *field, child,* or *held?*

A special spelling will often show consonants that are different from those in the word itself. Just think the sounds for the consonants in the special spelling. Look at the special spellings for these two words as they would appear in this book's glossary:

coax (kōks)   **chaise** (shāz)

Find out from the pronunciation key shown in this lesson what sounds to think for ō and ā. You already know the sounds that *k, s, sh,* and *z* usually stand for. If you use those sounds, you will know how to pronounce *coax* and *chaise.*

When you want to find out how to say a word correctly, these four steps will help you:

1. Find the word in the glossary at the back of this book or in a dictionary in your classroom or library.
2. Look at the special spelling for the word.
3. Use the pronunciation key to find out what sound any marked letter in the special spelling stands for.
4. Say the word to yourself. For the consonants in the special spelling, use the sounds that those

consonants usually stand for. For each vowel in the special spelling, use the vowel sound you hear in the key word for that vowel.

Discussion

Help your class answer these questions:

1. When will you need to know how to pronounce a word you meet in your reading? Why should you want to pronounce such a word correctly?

2. What two different things in a dictionary will you need to use to find out how to pronounce a word correctly? Where can you find each one? How do you use them to find out how to pronounce a word? What is the correct pronunciation of *wield?* What are the correct pronunciations of *coax* and *chaise?*

3. What does the glossary at the back of this book tell you is the correct pronunciation of each of the following words?

   choir   **queue**   **suede**   **plaque**   **sword**

4. Can you think of a sentence to show a right meaning and a right pronunciation for each of those words?

On your own

Some of the words in the paragraph below may be new to you. Try to get the right meaning for each new word from the context. Then use a dictionary or the glossary at the back of this book to check on the meaning of the word and to get its pronunciation.

Paul had lived near the ocean all his life. He could always find interesting things to do there. He liked to walk down to the quay and watch the ships being loaded at the piers. Sometimes he would see a yacht in the harbor. The harbor sights made Paul imagine the old days of sailing ships and pirates when the rogues hid their stolen treasure on desert isles. How Paul would have loved to sail away and search for a cache of pirate's gold! What an exciting adventure that would be!

Checking your work

If you are asked to do so, read aloud some of the sentences in the paragraph above. If you make a mistake pronouncing any word that you looked up, find out what you did wrong.

VARIETY

A chameleon, when he's feeling blue,
Can alter his glum point of view
  By changing his hue
  To a color that's new:
I'd like to do that, wouldn't you?

              — Eve Merriam

One day I went out to the zoo,
For I wanted to see the old gnu.
    But the old gnu was dead
    And the new gnu, they said,
Was too new a new gnu to view.

              — Miriam Troop

There was an old man with a beard
Who said, *"It is just as I feared!*
 Two Owls and a Hen,
 Four Larks and a Wren,
Have all built their nests in my beard!"

— EDWARD LEAR

YOU'RE ASKING ME?

A puppy whose hair was so flowing
There really was no means of knowing
 Which end was his head,
 Once stopped me and said,
"Please, sir, am I coming or going?"

— Oliver Herford

GOING

COMING

IS ANYBODY HOME?

235

April had been chosen from her Brownie troop in the city to go to a meeting on a farm. Many girls from other Brownie Scout troops would also be there, and April was looking forward to meeting them. She was very happy and excited as she arrived at the farm with Mrs. Cole and Flicker, the leaders of her Brownie troop.

HOW D.Y.B. WORKED FOR APRIL

by Marguerite de Angeli

The other cars had already arrived. The girls were laughing and talking like old friends, even though they had just met. Griz, one of the leaders, introduced each girl and leader to the others and then said:

"This little girl is Phyllis Merchant. She is visiting my neighbor, and though she isn't a Brownie, I know you will make her welcome. Perhaps she will like us so well that she will help start a Brownie Scout troop when she goes back home. Phyllis lives way out in the country and has no brothers or sisters. So we must show her what good sisters Brownies can be."

Phyllis smiled and turned her blue eyes on one girl after another. But when they fell on April, the smile began to fade. She drew her brows together in a slight frown and glanced away. April felt an unpleasant thud inside.

But Mrs. Cole said quickly, "Come, Mrs. Green is there waiting for us." She took April's hand, and they went through the white gate where Mrs. Green met them. She was a pretty lady and so pleasant that April soon forgot the look Phyllis had given her. She remembered the secret letters Mrs. Cole had whispered, "D.Y.B."

Leaving sweaters and coats on the wide porch, they all followed Mrs. Green to the big barn to see the animals. It stood on the rise of the hill so that it was on two levels.

"This is what they call a bank barn," Mrs. Green told them as they walked up the slope. "You see, the ground is filled in up to the large door so that the hay wagons can drive right into the barn."

She opened the big high doors. The girls walked in to the warm, sweet dark where the haylofts were. They were nearly empty now, for the haying season hadn't begun. Rays of sunlight sifted through cracks near the roof. April could hear pigeons cooing in the loft.

They went from one part of the barn to another, up ladders and down. Mrs. Green led them down to the floor of the lower barn. They could look out over a half-door into the yard where the cows stood. April had never been so close to a cow before in her life! She could have reached out and touched a cow's nose, but she didn't.

Flicker came and stood next to her. "See the barn swallows!" she said. "And there are the nests."

She showed April the little basket-shaped nests of clay which clung to the sides of the beams over the doorway. Sharp-tailed swallows darted about the barnyard, and April even saw one leaving the nest!

"They are eating their supper," said Flicker. "See how they catch the flies on the wing?" They made little mewing cries as they dipped and soared.

In another part of the barn they saw the horses. There were pigs in still another section of the barn. Right near was the pen where a little new calf lay. He was so new that when he stood up he was still trembly on his legs.

Mrs. Cole said, "He looks like every other baby thing, doesn't he?" April could see what she meant.

Mrs. Green had set the table out on the lawn where it looked over the meadow and away off to the blue hills beyond. The air was as warm as summer. Mrs. Green had prepared a fire in the outdoor fireplace, and now one of the leaders was helping her broil the meat.

While the cooking was being done, the girls played tag or pushed one another in the swing that hung from the oak tree. April sat on the porch and played with the kittens. There was a whole basketful! There were nine of them, all different. The mother cat sat near the door with her tail slowly moving back and forth. Her ears were cocked forward, as if she were not too sure that her children were safe.

When it was time to go to the table, April was last to find a seat.

"Here, child, sit here!" called Mrs. Green.

April went to the table. Just as she stepped over the long bench to sit down, the little girl sitting in the next place turned around. It was Phyllis! She looked at April and started to get up.

"I'm not going to sit there next to ——" She got no further, for there was Mrs. Green, who had followed April to help her find her seat.

Mrs. Green clapped her hands over Phyllis's thoughtless mouth. She helped Phyllis to rise and then led her away into the house. Griz quickly followed. Mrs. Cole was near at hand, too. She gently led April down the hill out of sight of the others, who had been so busy chattering that they hadn't heard what Phyllis said.

"Dear child," Mrs. Cole said as she and April walked together. "Remember D.Y.B. It means allowing for the thoughtlessness of others as well as trying to be thoughtful yourself. It means being forgiving because someone else doesn't know what she is saying."

Mrs. Cole stroked April's hair as she talked. With her quiet voice and gentle way, she helped April to swallow the lump in her throat. April began to feel sorry for Phyllis when Mrs. Cole told her that Phyllis had no mother.

"Now," said Mrs. Cole, "will you promise to try to forget that Phyllis didn't want to sit near you? Will you show her what a true Scout is like? Come on, now, up with the corners of your mouth! Remember, it's your birthday!"

Phyllis wasn't very friendly to April during the meal. But one of the leaders sat between them, and April enjoyed the broiled kabobs which she had never eaten before. They were pieces of meat, tomato, and onion. They had been put on long pins, called skewers, and broiled over the open fire. Everyone made April feel as if it were a birthday party just for her. They sang the birthday song. There was even a cake Mrs. Green had made and put candles on. April cut the first piece. She was happy.

The Storm

The sky began to cloud. A chill wind blew before they had finished eating, but Mrs. Green said, "It's April, don't forget. What if we do have a shower? It won't last long. We'll gather things up and go into the house. Then we can have a sing in front of the fireplace."

What fun it was! The fireplace was large, and there was room on the floor for all the girls. They hardly heard the deep roll of thunder that was followed by a sudden spatter of rain against the windows. The walls were thick and stout. April felt safe with such warm friends about. Even Phyllis began to move near her as they sat on the floor. She looked curiously into April's face for a moment. Then she timidly touched April's hand with a fingertip.

Suddenly Flicker said, "I believe the storm is getting worse. Listen!" There was a flash of lightning and a roar of wind and rain, followed by a crash of thunder.

"You can't go home in this!" Mrs. Green exclaimed. "You'll have to stay all night!"

"Sixteen people stay all night! Where would you put us?" laughed Flicker. "Nonsense! We

will wait awhile till the storm lessens. Then we can go."

Mr. Green brought in popcorn and long-handled poppers to use over the bed of coals left from the fire. April thought it was wonderful to be caught away from home in the storm. But

Phyllis whimpered, "I wish it would stop. I wish we could go home. I wish the thunder would stop." She moved nearer to April.

The storm went on and on. Mr. Green went out to see if there was any sign of its stopping.

"It wouldn't be safe to start home in this," he said. "We can find enough beds and blankets for all of you. You'll have to stay."

At first it seemed out of the question. But Mr. Green helped Griz do the telephoning to let the girls' parents know they were safe. Mrs. Green and Mrs. Cole and Flicker found bedding upstairs. It didn't look so impossible after all. "This house is much too large for two people anyway," Mr. Green said. "And it hasn't seen enough of overnight crowding!"

Mrs. Green helped the girls get ready for bed. She put April into the same room as Phyllis and two other girls. The other girls got themselves ready and into the big bed first. Flicker helped Phyllis to get comfortable on the couch by the window.

The small bed was for April. Mrs. Cole tucked her in and whispered, "You *did* remember to live up to the secret letters, didn't you? You are a brave girl. Did you have a nice birthday?"

"Oh, yes," whispered April, "wonderful!"

"I know now that when you leave our troop to 'fly up' to the next group, you will still remember D.Y.B. Don't forget! *Always* D.Y.B.!" Mrs. Cole kissed April good night, put out the light, and closed the door.

The storm howled and beat upon the windowpanes. The lightning flashed and filled the room with brightness, and the rolling thunder shook the roof.

Phyllis began to whimper again. April was going to call out to her that everything was all right. But then she remembered Phyllis's look. April just lay still and wondered if her family missed her at home.

The other two girls were quiet, and April knew they were asleep.

April could hear Phyllis moving. She heard her sigh. She thought how lonely Phyllis must be with no mother. She felt sorry for her and wanted to go and comfort her. But then she remembered how Phyllis had refused to sit beside her at the table. So she turned over, pulling the covers over her ears. April fell asleep.

Some time later, April felt something. She half awoke. Then came a whisper, "It's me — Phyllis. I'm cold, and I'm *so* lonesome. Can't I talk to you?" April was awake now.

"Of course," she answered.

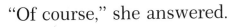

Phyllis was quiet for a moment. Then she said hesitantly, "You know, at first I didn't like you. I never knew anyone just like you before. But Flicker told me about you and how nice you were. She told me how much you know about birds and trees, too. And she says you like to read books. So do I. I read all the time. I like fairy tales best. Do you?"

She didn't wait for April to answer, but went on as if she couldn't wait to get it all out at once. "When I touched your hand that time, I felt how nice and smooth it was." She stopped for a moment and then went on, "I like you now." She breathed a deep sigh. She lay down again on the couch and went sound asleep!

April sighed, too. What a wonderful birthday it had been!

When she awoke in the morning, April couldn't think where she was. There was no sound of cars going over pavements, and no sound of huge trucks shaking the house as they passed. Instead, there were chickens muttering to themselves, cows mooing, the faraway barking of a dog, and — just as at home — birds singing.

Then she remembered the farm and Phyllis, her new friend.

The storm was over, and bright sunshine filled the new-washed world.

As the girls dressed, they chattered as if their whole lives depended on their getting to know each other in the short time they would be together.

"And I'll write to you," Phyllis went on, "and you can write to me, and we can tell each other what we're reading and everything. I'll try reading some of those books you told me about."

"Yes," agreed April, "and I'll try reading fairy tales, too. And you can tell me about the Brownie Scout troop you're going to join. I can tell you about the real Girl Scout troop I'm going to 'fly up' to, and — "

"Yes," Phyllis began again, not even waiting for April to stop. "I know my daddy would like me to be a Brownie. But tell me, what does D.Y.B. mean?"

"That's a secret," said April. "I can't tell that. But if you join a Brownie troop, you'll find out!"

Just then, Griz called up the stairs for the girls to stop talking and hurry down. Phyllis was ready first so she ran on ahead while April finished combing her hair. April thought to herself about "D.Y.B." and how remembering those secret letters had helped her. By remembering them she had made Phyllis her friend. Phyllis had no mother and no brothers or sisters, and she needed friends. It paid to DO YOUR BEST!

It was fun having breakfast in the big farm kitchen. Phyllis chose the seat on one side of April. The table was stretched to its full length, and there was room for everybody.

"I promised all your mothers that you would be home early this morning," said Flicker, "so we must start soon."

Phyllis and April said good-by to each other and promised to write. Then came the ride home through the fresh, cold air.

"Oh," thought April, "it's all much better than
I thought it *could* be, and it's lasting longer, too.
Besides, I have a new friend!"

It was still early when they reached home.
April told Mamma all about it.

"You see, Mamma," April exclaimed, "Phyllis
didn't know the truth about me at all! She didn't
know at first that my skin is just like hers, only
a different color. And she didn't know how I like
to read just as she does! I guess if she had known
the truth about me, she would have liked me at

first!" April laughed as she remembered her new friend.

"Yes," agreed Mamma soberly. "Yes, that is just it, exactly. She didn't know the truth. We must know *the truth*, always!"

AUTHOR

The story by Marguerite de Angeli that you have just read is from her well-known book, *Bright April*.

Marguerite Lofft de Angeli was born in Michigan. When Marguerite was thirteen, the Lofft family moved to Philadelphia, Pennsylvania. A few years later, she married John de Angeli, and the de Angelis had five children. It was not until after she was married that Mrs. de Angeli began to study drawing. She then began to write and illustrate stories for children.

Marguerite de Angeli is the author and illustrator of many, many books. You may have seen her beautiful *Mother Goose* book. Some of her books that you may enjoy reading now are:

Copper-Toed Boots   *Skippack School*
Just Like David   *Thee, Hannah!*
Henner's Lydia   *Yonie Wondernose*

One of her other books, *The Door in the Wall,* won the prized Newbery Medal in 1950. In 1968, Mrs. de Angeli received another honor called the Regina Medal. This was given to her for her lifetime of outstanding writing for children.

START OF A STORM

The trees
go wild,
yellow stabs
the sky,
awnings leap,
papers fly—
and suddenly,
with a rattling cry
against the pane
roars
the rain!

-Lou Ann Welte

What's the Matter with Kerby?

by Scott Corbett

Peterson Park was a small public park, but it seemed large to Kerby Maxwell — especially when he was at the far end of it and already late for supper.

He turned and whistled to his dog Waldo.

"Come on!" cried Kerby as he rushed away with Waldo at his heels.

As he rounded a curve in the path, he pulled up short. Alongside the path not far from the drinking fountain was a drain with a small iron grating over it. An old lady had the heel of her shoe caught in the drain.

"Oh! Oh! Help me, someone," she was saying.

She was a strange-looking old lady. Her hat was large and had an enormous feather trailing from it. She wore a draggly black cape over a draggly black dress.

"Here, little boy! Will you help me, please?"

Even though he was late for supper, Kerby said, "Yes, ma'am," and hurried forward. The old lady took her foot out of the shoe and stood balancing herself on one foot while Kerby bent down and pulled at the shoe. Kerby worked the shoe loose, and she put her foot back into it.

"Thank you. Thank you very much," she said, in a voice that made her sound a bit like a trained crow. "What's your name?"

"Kerby Maxwell, ma'am."

"Well, I'm Mrs. Graymalkin, Kerby, and I must say you've been a little gentleman. One doesn't meet many little gentlemen these days. I wish I could do something for you. In fact, you remind me a lot of my Felix when he was your age. Poor little Felix!" she said, and sniffed sadly.

"What's the matter, Mrs. Graymalkin?" asked Kerby. "Did he die?"

"No. He grew up!" she declared, as though this had been quite thoughtless of him.

"That's too bad," said Kerby.

"I've never forgiven him," she admitted. She laid a bony finger alongside her nose. "In fact, I know what I'll do. I'm going to give you one of his favorite toys, Kerby — one he used to play with by the hour. Do you like magic, Kerby?"

"Sure!"

"And do you like chemistry?"

"I guess so," said Kerby uncertainly. "I don't know much about it."

"You'll like it," Mrs. Graymalkin assured him. "I'm going to give you Felix's old magic chemistry set. You can do all sorts of flibbertygibbety tricks with it. I'll bring it to the park tomorrow at this same time and give it to you."

"That's very nice of you," said Kerby politely. "But I wonder if you could bring it a little earlier, so I won't be late for supper?"

"Oh? What time do you have supper?"

"The same time as tonight — and I'm already late tonight."

"Oh, my goodness — Well, then, I won't keep you. I'll be here tomorrow night at, say, a quarter to six. Now run along!"

"Yes, ma'am!" said Kerby, and he dashed away with Waldo at his side. "Let's go, boy! We're *really* late now!"

The next day, Kerby and Waldo almost did not get to the park at all.

They were in disgrace.

Kerby was in disgrace for being late to supper, and for spilling a glass of milk at breakfast, and for playing with his food at lunch, and for not cleaning up the workbench in the basement as his father had been after him to do for three days now.

As for Waldo, he was in disgrace for chewing one leaf off the plant Kerby's mother was trying to raise (it only had two leaves to begin with) and for digging a hole in the flower bed.

Kerby had to spend all morning making a start at giving the basement a good cleaning. Somehow he didn't get far with it. When his mother came down and saw how much time he had managed to waste, she shook her head severely.

After lunch he still had to stay in. But he sat around where his mother could see him, trying to look pale and unhealthy, so that she would realize how much he needed some fresh air and sunshine.

Finally she took pity on him.

She told him he could go out and play for a little while, but if he came in late for supper again, he would not set foot out of the house for a whole week and that was a promise.

"Don't worry, Mom, I won't be late again," he said, shooting out of the door like a rocket. He whistled for Waldo, and they hurried to the park.

In the park Kerby met a couple of boys he knew, and Waldo met a couple of dogs he knew, so for a while they just played. Then Kerby remembered about Mrs. Graymalkin and hurried along the path to the drinking fountain.

Here came Mrs. Graymalkin. She was wearing the same clothes as yesterday — hat, feather, cape, and all —and when she saw Kerby, she smiled. He tried quickly to count how many gaps there were between her teeth. There were at least five or six. There were almost more gaps than there were teeth.

"Well, Kerby dear! I'm glad to see you came."

"Yes, ma'am. Did you — " he began, and then stopped. After all, it wasn't very polite to ask right away if she had brought the chemistry set.

Mrs. Graymalkin cackled. It was her way of laughing, Kerby decided.

"Oh, never fear! I didn't forget it!" she said, patting her cape. Reaching around under it, she pulled out a long wooden box. "Here's the gift I promised you!"

The outside of the box was plain, but on the inside of the lid, when she lifted it, Kerby read:

FEATS O' MAGIC CHEMISTRY SET

Arranged in a row inside were corked glass tubes full of liquids. Each tube had a faded label on it. In one

section of the box were eyedroppers and several glass beakers, with measurements on their sides, for mixing things in.

There was also a small booklet. The title on its cover was *One Thousand and One Tricks to Do With Your FEATS O' MAGIC Chemistry Set.*

"Wow! That certainly looks interesting," said Kerby, anxious to get his hands on the set.

Mrs. Graymalkin's bony fingers picked one tube from its place and held it under his nose.

"Here's one of the best ones. My Felix loved to use this one," she said. "Fill a beaker half full of water. Add two drops of this. The water will start to boil and bubble and steam, but it won't get the least bit hot. You can even drink it down without hurting yourself at all. Everybody will be amazed!"

"They sure will," agreed Kerby, picturing his mother's and father's faces if he pulled a stunt like that. "That sounds like a good trick. I'll try it."

"You do that," said Mrs. Graymalkin, laughing delightedly. "I hope you have fun, Kerby, and I hope we'll meet here in the park again some day, so you can tell me all about it."

"Sure, Mrs. Graymalkin. Thanks!" he said.

"Carry it carefully!"

"I will. Good-by!" Kerby waved back at her as he hurried away along the walk. "Come on, Waldo!"

It would be better if his parents didn't know anything about the set, Kerby decided. Maybe later on, after he had gotten the hang of a few tricks, he would give them a show. But for now, the safest thing would be not to let anyone else know about the set. He decided to hide it in the garage for the night.

Through the kitchen windows, he could see the clock over the stove. Ten minutes till six. He ran into the house. His parents glanced around and were relieved to see that he was not going to get into trouble again tonight.

"Well!" said his mother. "Aren't you the good boy!"

"Sure!" said Kerby, pleased with himself. "What are we having for dinner?"

The Strangely Delightful Chemical

The next morning Kerby waited around the house, watching for a chance to take the chemistry set up to his room. At breakfast his mother had said something about wanting to go shopping that morning. If she did, he would have a chance to play with the set without having to worry.

To stay out of her sight as much as possible, he went into the garage. Waldo came along to keep him company.

As he was walking to the shelves to make sure the set was still there, Kerby accidentally bumped into the lawn mower handle. The lawn mower rolled backwards a few inches, making a noisy clatter on the floor.

"Shh!" he said fiercely, grabbing it. "Want to get me in trouble?"

If his mother heard the lawn mower, it might remind her to tell him to mow the lawn.

He was peeking at the chemistry set and showing it to Waldo, who sniffed it cautiously, when he heard the screen door slam.

"Kerby!" called his mother.

He covered up the set and came out of the garage as she walked down the back steps. She was all dressed up to go downtown shopping.

"That garage could use a good cleaning. And when are you going to finish the basement?"

"Aw, Mom, do I have to do that today?"

"No, not today," said his mother, pulling on her white gloves.

Kerby felt relieved.

"Today," his mother continued, "I want you to mow the lawn."

"Aw!"

"You heard me. It's been needing it for days. If you finish before I get back, you may play in the park — but only after you've finished. Now get started on the lawn. I want to see you start before I leave."

Grumbling to himself, Kerby rolled the lawn mower outside and began pushing it up and down the yard while his mother was backing the car out. As soon as she was gone, Kerby gave the lawn mower a good kick.

"*That's* for reminding her," he told it and sat down in the grass to think. Before he cut any more grass, he decided, he would take the chemistry set to his room.

Once there, he put it on his desk and examined everything in the box. All the chemicals smelled either funny or awful, and two or three made his eyes water. Waldo sneezed and left the room. Furthermore, he refused to come back. Kerby went after him

266

and even dragged him part way along the hall, but Waldo struggled and escaped from him.

"Oh, all right, *don't* come back," said Kerby as he returned to his room alone. He decided to try just one trick before going back to his lawnmowing.

He remembered what Mrs. Graymalkin had told him about how to make water bubble and boil without its becoming hot. That sounded like a good trick. He found that tube and uncorked it again for another sniff. It had an odd smell.

Kerby took a beaker to the bathroom and filled it half full of water. Returning to his room, he opened the same tube again and thrust an eyedropper into it. He pulled a tiny bit of the liquid into the eyedropper. Carefully he squeezed the chemical into the water.

Nothing happened.

No bubbling.

No boiling.

No steaming.

The water just sat there doing nothing. It was very disappointing.

Kerby sighed and decided to empty the beaker in the bathroom. After that, he would try a couple of the other tricks, just to see if any of them would work. Probably the chemicals were old and had lost all their fizz, but maybe some of them were still good. He might as well try.

As he walked down the hall, he held the water up to the light. He sniffed it to see if the chemical gave it any smell.

Kerby stopped. The water had a strangely delightful smell. Before he knew what he was doing, he obeyed a powerful urge.

He lifted the beaker to his lips and drank its contents.

The instant he did this, Kerby was scared.

He remembered the story *Dr. Jekyll and Mr. Hyde* and what had happened to Dr. Jekyll when he began to mess around with *his* chemistry set. Dr. Jekyll had drunk some stuff he had mixed up. The next thing he knew, he had changed into a horrible, hairy man who went out and did all sorts of terrible things. It made him bad, very bad.

With a scared cry, Kerby rushed into the bathroom to look at himself in the mirror. Would he change into a monster before his very own eyes?

Can This Be Kerby?

When Kerby looked in the mirror, however, all he saw was his own pale face. It was about six shades whiter than he had ever seen it before, but nothing else was different about it.

He stuck out his tongue, half expecting to see little toadstools growing all over it, but his tongue looked all right, too.

Then all at once his eyes rolled in circles, twice, and a strange feeling overcame him.

He felt good.

That was the only way to describe it. Good. Very good.

When Waldo had heard Kerby's scared cry, he came running to see what was the matter.

By the time he arrived, that good feeling had come over Kerby. He was washing out the beaker and drying it on a paper towel. Waldo stared up at him questioningly. Kerby patted his best friend gently on the head.

"Waldo, I want to apologize for dragging you down the hall," he said. "That is a mean thing to do, and I won't do it again. Besides, your nails scratch Mom's floors. In fact, they may already have done so from time to time. Later on, I must remember to polish the floors for her."

Waldo reared back and gave Kerby a worried look.

"I must put away my chemistry set now and not try any more experiments with it up here in my room," he told Waldo. "After all, this is no place to play with chemicals. I might spill some and mark my furniture. Besides, this is no time to be fooling around playing. I have work to do."

So saying, Kerby went outside and finished mowing the lawn. When his mother came home, she found him down in the cellar finishing up his cleaning job there.

"What a wonderful job you did on the lawn!" she

said, coming downstairs to stare at him in amazement. "I never saw such a good job!"

"I was glad to do it, Mom," said Kerby.

"And now, to find you working down here — Kerby, do you feel all right?"

"I feel good, Mom," he said. "Very good."

"Well . . ." His mother still looked doubtful, but she rose and started upstairs. "I'll fix some lunch, and — "

"It's already fixed, Mom," said Kerby, causing his

mother to stumble and nearly fall on her face, she was so surprised. "I thought I'd have it all ready for you when you came home."

After lunch he worked in the basement again all afternoon. Every once in a while his mother called down in an anxious tone to make sure he was all right. Around three o'clock she even telephoned his father.

When Kerby finally came upstairs, his father had just come home from work. Mr. Maxwell looked at him in a nervous way and laughed a hollow laugh.

"Well, son! Well . . . What have you been doing today?" he asked in what was probably supposed to be a jolly tone of voice.

Kerby told him.

His parents glanced at each other. "Kerby, I want to take your temperature," said his mother.

Now, ordinarily Kerby would have bucked like a steer at the idea of having his temperature taken, or swallowing a pill, or anything like that. But this time he simply smiled in a perfectly agreeable way.

"If you want to, Mom, please do, but I really do feel good. Very good."

His mother took his temperature. It was normal. She and his father kept handing the thermometer back and forth and staring at it as if they didn't believe it.

"I'm perfectly all right," Kerby assured them. "Want me to set the table, Mom?"

"Why . . . yes, I guess so," gasped his mother, hardly able to believe her ears.

At dinner, he was very careful about his manners and didn't spill any milk or play with his food one little bit. After dinner Kerby offered to dry the dishes.

"No, thanks! NO!" said his mother, almost crying. "Go out and play. You've done enough work for one day. I want you to go out and play!"

"May I go to the park?"

"Yes!"

"Thanks, Mom. I'll be home before dark."

Kerby ran over to the park, where he was very nice to all the other children. Before dark, Kerby was home again.

"Do you want to watch TV for a while?" his mother asked.

"No, I think I'll go up and start reading a book for my summer book report," he told her and ran upstairs. The clatter behind him in the living room was the sound of his father's pipe falling out of his mouth.

That night, when it was his bedtime, Kerby did not go to bed and read comic books with a flashlight under the covers as usual. This time his light went out promptly, and Kerby settled down at once.

"After all," he murmured to Waldo, "a boy my age needs his sleep."

Just Another Phase

"Kerby! Time for breakfast!"

Kerby opened one eye, and sunlight streamed into it, making him squint and close it again.

He rolled over and cautiously opened the other eye, remembering the different things that had happened yesterday. All the work he had done and everything.

"Kerby?"

"Yes, Mom."

It was his mother calling from downstairs. The way her voice sounded, you could tell she was wondering what to expect from him this morning.

Kerby wondered himself.

He sat up carefully in bed, terrified for fear he might feel the urge to start doing more chores. He heard the rattle of Waldo's toenails on the stairs.

"Come here, boy!"

Waldo crept into the room with a worried look in his eyes and cocked his head at Kerby, looking him over.

Kerby climbed out of bed and walked over to him. All at once he reached down, grabbed Waldo, and spun him around.

Waldo barked joyfully, and for a moment they battled wildly. Waldo was so pleased that he raced up and down the hall and in and out of every room.

Kerby was pleased, too.

"Well, I guess I'm all right," he decided.

When he came down for breakfast, both his parents looked at him in a funny way. His father cleared his throat and put down the morning paper.

"Well, good morning, son," he said. "By the way, while I think of it — I understand your mother mentioned to you yesterday that the garage could stand a good cleaning —"

"Aw, Pop, do I have to do it today?" asked Kerby.

His father sat back and glanced at his mother. They both looked relieved.

"No, no, not today, son," Mr. Maxwell assured him. "Just some day. You did quite a job around here yesterday."

Kerby's mother put her hand on his forehead.

"He's perfectly normal," she said happily.

"Good!"

"I guess it was just another phase," she said. Whatever Kerby did, they always seemed to say he was "going through a phase." It was one of those things parents say about children.

"I'm okay, Mom," he assured her.

Naturally, he had realized the terrible truth about that stuff he had mixed up and drunk.

It had made him *good*.

It had made him be good and do good deeds all day. But at least the magic seemed to last only one day. A good night's sleep had cured him.

Kerby shuddered to think what it would have been like if it had made him be good forever!

This was only the beginning of the fun Kerby had with his magic chemistry set. This story was taken from The Lemonade Trick, *by Scott Corbett. Some other books about Kerby are* The Baseball Trick, The Limerick Trick, The Turnabout Trick, The Disappearing Dog Trick, *and* The Mailbox Trick.

AUTHOR

The Lemonade Trick was the first of the "Trick" books. Scott Corbett recalls, "I began to write it one day when I found myself thinking about a small public park I played in when I was a boy. The first thing I knew, Kerby Maxwell was playing in that park, and staying later than he should, just the way I used to do. But I never met an old lady there quite like Mrs. Graymalkin, and I certainly never had a chemistry set like Kerby's!"

Mr. and Mrs. Corbett live in Providence, Rhode Island, and have one daughter. The Corbetts like to travel, and once they sailed around the world on a freighter. Another time they took an ocean trip around Cape Horn at the tip of South America.

In 1962, Scott Corbett's book, *Cutlass Island,* was chosen the best mystery for children by the Mystery Writers of America. Other books by Mr. Corbett that you will enjoy are *The Case of the Gone Goose, The Case of the Fugitive Firebug, Pippa Passes,* and *Ever Ride a Dinosaur?*

TRUTH OR Fantasy?

In the story you have just read, Kerby had a lot of fun with a magic chemistry set, especially when he drank one of the magic chemicals.

Does that mean it would be fun for YOU to drink a chemical from your chemistry set? NO! Not unless you'd enjoy a lot of pain and a quick trip to the hospital!

When you read, it's important for you to be able to judge what is true, or at least true-to-life.

In this book, the story about Henry Ford is *true*. It tells about a person who really lived and something that really happened. The story, "Golden Boy," did not really happen. The author made it up. But we call it a *true-to-life* story because it is about something that *could* have happened.

"What's the Matter With Kerby?" is not about a real person, and the story could not possibly have happened. We call a story like this a *fantasy*.

Each group of sentences below describes part of a story. Which of these do you think would be true-to-life stories, and which would be fantasy?

1. Two boys are camping out in the backyard. They are terrified by what looks like a ghost floating around in the

darkness. Then they discover that the ghost is a white sheet, blowing in the breeze on the clothesline.

2. A man's ship sinks in a storm at sea, and he swims to an island. He is so tired that he falls asleep at once. When he wakes up, he finds himself tied to the ground. All around him are tiny men six inches tall!

3. A boy had always wanted to be a baseball player. He was very small for his age, and the other boys teased him. But he was willing to work hard, and he practiced baseball whenever he could. In a few years, he became very strong in spite of his small size. In high school he played shortstop on the team. He is now one of the best ball players in the country.

4. While she is on a journey underground, a little girl finds

a bottle. Tied to the bottle is a label with the words, "DRINK ME." When she obeys, she feels herself growing smaller and smaller.

5. A traveler in a strange land has stopped to rest in a cave. Suddenly a horrible-looking giant walks into the cave. The giant has only one eye, right in the middle of his forehead.

6. David had always been interested in the moon. When he was a boy, he read books about the moon, and he often looked at the moon through his small telescope. His big dream was to get close enough to the moon to take good pictures of it. Now David is grown and is an astronaut. His dream comes true when he and two other astronauts are sent on a trip to the moon. David is chosen to take the pictures.

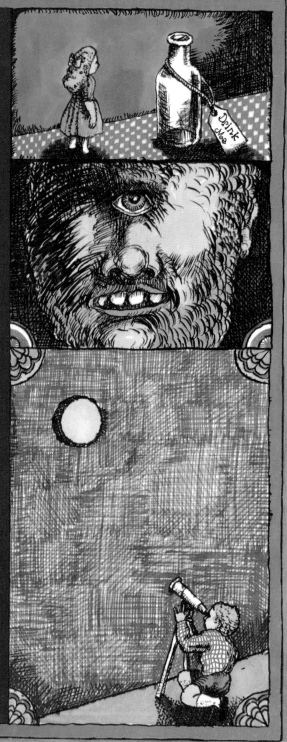

A Tongue Twister

Betty Botta bought some butter;
"But," said she, "This butter's bitter!
If I put it in my batter,
It will make my batter bitter.
But a bit o' better butter
Will but make my batter better."
So she bought a bit o' butter
Better than the bitter butter,
Made her bitter batter better.
So 'twas better Betty Botta
Bought a bit o' better butter.

**Skill
Lesson 6:**

UNDERSTANDING AND USING STRESS MARKS

You have learned how to use the special spellings in a glossary or a dictionary to find out how to pronounce a word that has just one syllable. But when a word has more than one syllable, there's something else you need to know.

You know that a word has as many syllables as there are vowel sounds in it. The word *come* has just one syllable, but the word *become* has two syllables. When you say a word that has more than one syllable, you say one of those syllables a little louder or with more force than the other syllables. Say *become* to yourself and listen to hear which of its two syllables you say with the greater force. It's the second one, isn't it? Now do the same thing with the word *welcome.* In *welcome,* it's the first syllable that you say with more force, or **stress,** isn't it?

Now look at those same two words as they are shown in one dictionary:

be·come (bĭ kŭm′)

wel·come (wĕl′kəm)

Notice the mark that comes right after the *m* in the special spelling for *become*. You can see that same mark after the *l* in the special spelling for *welcome*. That mark (′) is a **stress mark.** It tells you that the syllable just before it should be said with more force than the other syllable or syllables.

You don't have to worry, of course, about stress marks for words you already know. You just say them the way you've heard them said many times. But when you meet a longer word that you haven't heard before, or one that you aren't sure about, noticing the stress mark in a dictionary will help you pronounce that word correctly. By putting the stress in the right place when you say a word, you will help other people understand quickly what you're saying.

Some words that are spelled just alike are said in different ways and have different syllables and meanings depending on which part of the word is stressed. When that is true, you will find the same word listed twice with different special spellings. You will need to look at the meanings for each one to find out how the word should be pronounced in what you are reading.

Look at this sentence:

Bill's mother asked him to take out the **refuse.**

You may know that when the word in heavy black print is pronounced one way, it means "say no." If you do, you can see that this meaning doesn't make sense in the sentence. If you looked for the word in a dictionary, here is what you might find:

re·fuse (ri fyo͞oz′) Say "no."

ref·use (ref′yo͞os)   Junk, or trash.

You can see that the second meaning makes sense in the sentence. In reading the sentence, then, you should use the pronunciation that has the second meaning. Can you read the sentence now the way it should sound?

Most dictionaries have the stress mark coming right after the syllable that should be stressed. Some dictionaries, however, place the stress mark *before* the syllable that should be stressed. In the front part of every dictionary is a full explanation of all the marks used by that dictionary to show correct pronunciations. Before you look up any word in a dictionary to learn how to pronounce it, check that explanation to find out how that dictionary shows which syllable should be stressed.

Discussion

Help your class answer these questions:

1. Where in a dictionary will you find stress marks?
2. Why do you need to know what a stress mark means?
3. What does a stress mark tell you to do?
4. What should you do if you find the same word listed twice in a dictionary with a different syllable stressed each time?
5. What two ways of showing where the stress falls are used in different dictionaries? How can you find out which way is used by a particular dictionary?
6. You already know how to pronounce each of the words printed in separate syllables below. Where would you place a stress mark in each one to show someone how to say it correctly?

com·mand   ther·mom·e·ter

cor·ral   chem·i·cal

prop·er·ty   ex·pen·sive

On your own

Read the paragraph that follows. Try to use the context to get the meaning of each word that is shown in heavy black print and that may be new to you. Then use the glossary at the back of this book to check on those meanings and to find the correct pronunciations of the words. Be sure to stress the correct syllables as you say each new word to yourself.

Eddie had always wanted to see his favorite pitcher in person, and he had been excited about going to the game with his neighborhood team. But he got sick with the **measles** and had to stay in bed that day. That's why he was in such **despair** while his friends were at the game. How he wished the game were being **televised** so that he could see what was happening! He turned on the radio at game time and tried to make **mental** pictures of the things he heard. It sounded like a **sensational** game. Eddie's favorite pitcher was a **hero** that day. Eddie's dad tried to cheer him up when he saw how unhappy Eddie was. He

said, "Eddie, you'll forget all about this in a few days. Besides, you can go to a game some other time." But Eddie wasn't **consoled** by those words. He knew that he would NEVER forget the **miserable** day he missed the game.

Now read the sentences that follow. Use the glossary to get the correct pronunciations for the words in heavy black print. Choose the pronunciations that have the correct meanings in these sentences.

1. The horse wasn't able to make much **progress** in the blinding snowstorm.
2. Bill told his friend Jim, "Mom said that you're invited to stay for supper if your mother doesn't **object.**"
3. "You're doing well with baseball, David," said his teacher. "If you practice often and try to **perfect** your pitching, you may be a star player someday."

Checking your work

If you are asked to do so, read aloud a sentence in which there is a word in heavy black print. Find out if others agree that you used the right pronunciation for that word. If you made a mistake, find out why it was a mistake.

McBroom Tells the Truth
by Sid Fleischman

Here is a tall tale to beat them all!

There has been so much tomfool nonsense told about McBroom's wonderful one-acre farm that I had better set matters straight. I'm McBroom. Josh McBroom. I'll explain about the watermelons in a minute.

I aim to put down the facts, one after the other, the way things happened — exactly.

It began, you might say, the day we left the farm in Connecticut. We piled our youngsters and everything we owned into our old air-cooled Franklin automobile. We headed west.

To count noses, besides my own, there was my dear wife Melissa and our eleven red-headed youngsters.

Their names were Will*jill*hester*chester*peter*polly*tim-*tom*mary*larry*andlittle*clarinda*.

It was summer, and the trees along the way were full of birdsong. We had gotten as far as Iowa when my dear wife Melissa made a startling discovery. We had *twelve* children along — one too many! She had just counted them again.

I slammed on the brakes and raised a cloud of dust. "Will*jill*hester*chester*peter*polly*tim*tom*mary*larry*and-little*clarinda*!" I shouted. "Line up!"

The youngsters tumbled out of the car. I counted noses and there were twelve. I counted again. Twelve.

Once more I made the count — but this time I caught
Larry slipping around behind. He was having his
nose counted twice, and the mystery was solved. The
scamp! Didn't we laugh, though, and stretch our legs
in the bargain.

Just then a thin, long-legged man came ambling
down the road. He was so scrawny I do believe he
could have hidden behind a flagpole, ears and all. He
wore a tall, stiff collar, a diamond stickpin in his tie,
and a straw hat.

"Lost, neighbor?" he asked, eating a green apple.

"Not a bit," said I. "We're heading west, sir. We gave up our farm — it was half rocks and the other half tree stumps. Folks tell us there's land out west and the sun shines in the winter."

"You can't beat Iowa for farmland," said the stranger.

"Maybe so," I nodded. "But I'm short of funds. Unless they're giving farms away in Iowa, we'll keep a-going."

The man scratched his chin. "See here, I've got more land than I can plow. You look like nice folks. I'd like to have you for neighbors. I'll let you have eighty acres cheap. Not a stone or a tree stump anywhere on the place. Make an offer."

"Thank you kindly, sir," I smiled. "But I'm afraid you would laugh at me if I offered you everything in my billfold."

"How much is that?"

"Ten dollars exactly."

"Sold!" he said. "I'll write out the deed."

Well, I almost choked with surprise. I thought he must be joking, but quick as a wink he was scratching out a deed on the back of an old envelope.

"Hector Jones is my name, neighbor," he said. "You can call me Heck — everyone does."

Was there ever a more kindly and generous man? He signed the deed, and I gladly gave him my ten-dollar bill.

Mr. Heck Jones jumped on the running board and guided us a mile up the road.

Finally he raised his long arm and pointed.

"There's your property, neighbor," he said.

Didn't we tumble out of the car in a hurry? We gazed with delight at our new farm. It was broad and sunny with an oak tree on a gentle hill. There was one problem, to be sure. A marshy-looking pond spread across an acre beside the road. You could lose a cow in a place like that, but we had gotten a bargain — no doubt about it.

"Mama," I said to my dear Melissa. "See that fine oak on the hill? That's where we'll build a house."

"No, you won't," said Mr. Heck Jones. "That oak's not on your property."

"But, sir — "

"All that's yours is what you see under water. Not a rock or a tree stump in it, just as I said."

I thought he must be having his little joke, except that there wasn't a smile to be found on his face. "But *sir*!" I said. "You clearly stated that the farm was eighty acres."

"That's right."

"That marshy pond hardly covers an acre."

"That's wrong," he said. "There are a full eighty acres — one piled on the other, like pancakes. It's eighty acres deep, McBroom. Read the deed."

I read the deed. It was true.

"Hee-haw! Hee-haw!" he snorted. "I got the best of you, McBroom! Good day, neighbor."

He hurried away, laughing up his sleeve all the way home. I soon learned that Mr. Heck was always laughing up his sleeve. Folks told me that when he'd hang up his coat and go to bed, all that stored-up laughter would pour out his sleeve and keep him awake nights. But there's no truth to that.

I'll tell you about the watermelons in a minute.

The Whole Truth of the Matter

Well, there we stood gazing at our one-acre farm that wasn't good for anything but jumping into on a hot day. And that day was the hottest I could remember.

I turned to our children. "Will*jill*hester*chester*peter*polly*tim*tom*mary*larry*andlittle*clarinda*," I said. "There's always a bright side to things. That pond we bought is a bit muddy, but it's wet. Let's jump in and cool off."

We were soon in our swimming clothes. I gave the signal, and we took a running jump.

At that moment such a dry spell struck that we landed in an acre of dry earth.

The pond had evaporated! It was very surprising.

My boys had jumped in headfirst, and there was nothing to be seen of them but their legs kicking in the air. I had to pull them out of the earth like carrots. Some of my girls were still holding their noses.

But the moment I ran the topsoil through my fingers, my farmer's heart skipped a beat. That pond bottom felt as soft and rich as black silk. "My dear Melissa!" I called. "Come look! This topsoil is so rich it ought to be kept in a bank."

I was in a sudden fever of excitement. That rich topsoil seemed to cry out for seed. My dear Melissa

had a sack of dried beans along, and I sent Will and Chester to fetch it. I saw no need to bother plowing the field. I directed Polly to draw a straight row with a stick and Tim to follow her, poking holes in the ground. Then I came along. I dropped a bean in each hole and stamped on it with my heel.

Well, I had hardly gone a couple of yards when something green and leafy tangled my foot. I looked behind me. There was a beanstalk traveling along in a hurry and looking for a pole to climb on.

"Glory be!" I exclaimed. That soil was *rich*! The stalks were spreading out all over. I had to rush along to keep ahead of them.

By the time I got to the end of the row, the first stalks had blossomed and the beans were ready for picking.

You can imagine our excitement.

Within an hour we had planted and harvested the whole crop of beans. But it was hot working in the sun! I sent Larry to find a good acorn along the road. We planted it, but it didn't grow near as fast as I had expected. We had to wait three hours for a shade tree.

We made camp under our oak tree, and the next day we drove to Barnsville with our crop of beans. I traded it for seeds — carrot and squash and cabbage and others.

Of course, there was a secret to that topsoil. A government man came out to look into the matter. He said there had once been a huge lake in that part of Iowa. It had taken thousands of years to shrink up to our pond, as you can imagine. The lake fish must have been tightly packed in. There's nothing like fish in soil to make things grow. We did sometimes turn up a fish bone.

It wasn't long before Mr. Heck Jones came around to pay us a neighborly call. He was eating a raw turnip. When he saw the way we were planting and harvesting cabbage, his eyes popped out of his head. It almost cost him his eyesight.

He hurried away, muttering to himself.

"My dear Melissa," I said. "That man is up to no good. He'll be back."

Meanwhile, we went about our business on the farm. I don't mind saying that before long we were showing a handsome profit. Back in Connecticut we had been lucky to harvest one crop a year. Now we were planting and harvesting three or four crops a *day*.

But there were things we had to be careful about. Weeds, for one thing. My youngsters took turns standing weed guard. The instant a weed popped out of the ground, they'd race to it and hoe it to death. You can imagine what would happen if weeds ever got going in rich soil like ours.

But I don't want you to think there was nothing but work on our farm. Some crops we grew just for the fun of it. Take pumpkins. The vines grew so fast we could hardly catch the pumpkins. It was something to see. The youngsters used to wear themselves out running after those pumpkins. Sometimes they'd have pumpkin races.

Sunday afternoons, just for the sport of it, the older boys would plant a pumpkin seed and try to catch a ride. It wasn't easy. You had to grab hold the instant the blossom dropped off and the pumpkin began to swell. Whoosh! It would jerk you off your feet and take you whizzing over the farm until it wore itself out. Sometimes they'd use banana squash, which was faster.

We'd see Mr. Heck Jones standing on the hill in the distance, watching. He wasn't going to rest until he had run us off our land.

Then, late one night, I was awakened by hee-hawing and chuckling outside the house. I went to the window and saw old Heck in the moonlight. He was chuckling and heeing and hawing and sprinkling seed every which way.

I pulled off my sleeping cap and rushed outside.

"What are you up to, Neighbor Jones?" I shouted.

"Hee-haw!" he answered, and hurried away, laughing up his sleeve.

I had a sleepless night, as you can imagine. The next morning, as soon as the sun came up, that farm of ours broke out in weeds. You never saw such weeds! They came out of the ground and tumbled madly over each other. In no time at all, the weeds were in a tangle several feet thick and still rising.

We had a fight on our hands, I tell you! "Will*jill*hester-*chester*peter*polly*tim*tom*mary*larry*andlittle*clarinda*!" I shouted. "There's work to do!"

We started hoeing and hacking away. For every weed we uprooted, another took its place. We were a whole month fighting those weeds. If our neighbors hadn't pitched in to help, we'd still be there burning weeds.

The day finally came when the farm was cleared and up popped old Heck Jones. He was eating a big slice of watermelon. That's what I was going to tell you about.

"Howdy, Neighbor McBroom," he said. "I came to say good-by."

"Are you leaving, sir?" I asked.

"No, but *you* are."

I looked him squarely in the eye. "And if I don't, sir?"

"Why, hee-haw, McBroom! There's heaps more of weed seed where that came from!"

My dander was up. I rolled back my sleeves, meaning to give him a whipping he wouldn't forget. But what happened next saved me the bother.

As my youngsters gathered around, Mr. Heck Jones made the mistake of spitting out a mouthful of watermelon seeds. Things did happen fast!

Before I knew what he had done, a watermelon vine whipped up around old Heck's scrawny legs and jerked him off his feet. He went whizzing every which way over the farm. Watermelon seeds were flying. Soon he came zipping back and crashed into a pumpkin left over from Sunday. In no time, watermelons and pumpkins went galloping all over the place, and they were knocking him about something wild. He streaked here and there. Melons crashed and exploded. Old Heck was so covered with melon, he looked as if he had been shot out of a ketchup bottle. It was something to see!

Then the watermelons and pumpkins began to play themselves out. I figured Mr. Heck Jones would like to get home as fast as possible. So I asked Larry to fetch me the seed of a large banana squash.

"Hee-haw! Neighbor Jones," I said, and pitched the seed at his feet. I hardly had time to say "Good-by" before the vine had him. A long banana squash gave him a fast ride all the way home. I wish you could have been there to see it. He never came back.

That's the whole truth of the matter. Anything else you hear about McBroom's wonderful one-acre farm is an outright fib.

AUTHOR

Sid Fleischman loves American tall-tale humor. *McBroom and the Big Wind* and *McBroom's Ear* are other books about the McBroom family.

Mr. Fleischman's books have won several awards. *Chancy and the Grand Rascal* won the Silver Medal from the Commonwealth Club of California in 1967. *By the Great Horn Spoon!* was a Boys Clubs of America award winner in 1963 and was made into a movie called *Bullwhip Griffin.*

Mr. Fleischman lives with his wife and three children in California. Besides his books for boys and girls, he also writes screenplays for movies.

When he was younger, Mr. Fleischman wanted to be a magician, and he taught himself many magic tricks. Later he decided to write instead. He now says, "But once a magician always a magician, I guess. When I speak at schools or libraries, I can easily be talked into pulling a rabbit out of a hat."

MORE BOOKS TO ENJOY

BRONZEVILLE BOYS AND GIRLS, *by Gwendolyn Brooks.*
This is a book of poems especially about city children.

FAST SOONER HOUND, *by Arna Bontemps and Jack Conroy.*
This is a tall tale of a lop-eared hound that can outrun any train in the country.

FLASH, CRASH, RUMBLE, AND ROLL, *by Franklyn M. Branley.*
This book explains what happens during a thunderstorm.

THE HUNDRED DRESSES, *by Eleanor Estes.*
Wanda has only one dress, and her classmates think she is strange. It is not until Wanda has left town that they realize what a wonderful person she is.

MY MOTHER IS THE MOST BEAUTIFUL WOMAN IN THE WORLD, *by Becky Reyher.*
In this story of old Russia, a lost girl goes from village to village in search of her mother.

THE RED BALLOON, *by Albert Lamorisse.*
In this fantasy, a boy chases a balloon through the streets of Paris.

TICO AND THE GOLDEN WINGS, *by Leo Lionni.*
A bird feels sad because he is different from the other birds, until he realizes he is beautiful.

GLOSSARY

This glossary can help you find out meanings and pronunciations of words in this book that you may not know. Reading Skill Lessons 3 and 4 explain how to look up a word in a dictionary or a glossary in order to find that word's meaning or meanings. Reading Skill Lesson 5 tells how to figure out the correct pronunciation of a one-syllable word by using its special spelling and the pronunciation key. Reading Skill Lesson 6 explains how stress marks can help you pronounce words of more than one syllable.

The pronunciation key below is a full one that shows how to pronounce each consonant and vowel in a special spelling. There is also a short form of this pronunciation key at the bottom of every left-hand page.

Full Pronunciation Key

Consonant Sounds

/b/	bib	/k/	kick	/sh/	ship, dish
/ch/	church	/l/	lid, needle	/t/	tight
/d/	did	/m/	man, am	/th/	thin, path
/f/	fast, off	/n/	no, sudden	/*th*/	this, bathe
/g/	gag	/ng/	thing	/v/	vine, cave
/h/	hat	/p/	pop	/w/	with
/hw/	which	/r/	roar	/y/	yes
/j/	judge	/s/	see, miss	/z/	zebra, size
		/zh/	pleasure		

Vowel Sounds

/ă/	pat	/ĭ/	pit	/oi/	noise
/ā/	pay	/ī/	pie	/ou/	out
/âr/	care	/îr/	fierce	/o͝o/	took
/ä/	father	/ŏ/	pot	/o͞o/	boot
/ĕ/	pet	/ō/	toe	/ŭ/	cut
/ē/	be	/ô/	paw, for	/ûr/	turn

/yo͞o/ use

/ə/ about, silent, pencil, lemon, circus

This pronunciation key is adapted from *The American Heritage Dictionary of the English Language*, published by American Heritage Publishing Co., Inc., and Houghton Mifflin Company.

A

a·corn (ā′kôrn) Nut of an oak tree.

a·cre (ā′kər) Piece of land a little smaller than a football field.

a·jar (ə-jär′) Open a little way.

am·ble (ăm′bəl) Walk in a slow, easy way.

anx·ious (ăngk′shəs) Eager; worried.

ar·rive (ə-rīv′) Come; get to a place.

ar·ti·cle (är′tĭ-kəl) Something written that is part of a book, magazine, or newspaper.

as·sure (ə-shŏŏr′) 1. Say something to remove doubt or make someone certain; promise. 2. Make safe.

B

ba·nan·a squash (bə-năn′ə skwŏsh) Kind of squash that is long and yellow and looks somewhat like a banana. (See also **squash**.)

bar·gain (bär′gĭn) 1. Agreement. — **into the bargain.** Besides; at the same time. 2. Something offered to a buyer at a good price.

base·ment (bās′mənt) Lowest floor of a house or building, usually below the ground.

bat·ter (băt′ər) Hit hard again and again.

bat·ter (băt′ər) Player at bat.

bat·ter (băt′ər) Thick mixture used in cooking: *cake batter.*

beak·er (bē′kər) Glass jar or bottle with a lip on it for easy pouring: *Beakers are often used in chemistry.*

beam (bēm) 1. Long, heavy piece of wood or metal often used in building. 2. Look joyful; smile widely. 3. Shine; give off light. 4. Ray of light.

bea·ver (bē′vər) Animal having brown fur, a broad, flat tail, and very strong, sharp teeth: *Beavers use their teeth to cut wood with which they build dams.*

ă pat / ā pay / âr care / ä father / ĕ pet / ē be / ĭ pit / ī pie / îr fierce / ŏ pot / ō toe / ô paw, for / oi noise / ou out / ŏŏ took / ōō boot / th thin / *th* this / ŭ cut / ûr turn / yōō use / ə about / zh pleasure

blossom (blŏs′əm) 1. Flower, especially on a plant or tree that bears fruit. 2. Bloom; come into flower.

bri·er (brī′ər) Also **briar**. Plant or bush with sharp thorns.

broil (broil) Cook by holding or placing very near whatever is making the heat.

C

cache (kăsh) Secret place where something valuable is hidden.

calf (kăf) The young of a cow.

calf (kăf) Back part of a person's leg between the knee and the ankle.

calm (käm) Become quiet or not excited.

can·yon (kăn′yən) Deep valley with steep hills or mountains on either side.

cape (kāp) Sleeveless, coat-like garment worn over the shoulders.

cape (kāp) Point of land sticking out into a body of water.

car·go (kär′gō) Load of stuff carried by something such as a ship, train, or truck.

cau·tious (kô′shəs) Careful; not taking foolish chances.

chem·i·cal (kĕm′ĭ-kəl) Any stuff or substance much used in the study of chemistry.

chem·is·try (kĕm′ĭs-trē) The study of what substances are made of and the ways in which substances are different from each other.

chill (chĭl) 1. Cold. 2. Feeling of coldness. 3. Unfriendly. 4. Make cold; lower the temperature.

choir (kwīr) Group of singers.

chug (chŭg) Make a short, repeated sound: *Engines often make a chugging sound.*

cir·cle (sûr′kəl) 1. Line so drawn that every point on it is the same distance from another point called the center. 2. Move in a circle. 3. Group of people with the same interests.

clerk (klûrk) Person who waits on shoppers in a store.

clutch (klŭch) 1. Tight hold. 2. Grab and hold onto. 3. Part of a car.

com·mand (kə-mănd′) Give someone an order to do something.

con·sole (kən-sōl′) Cheer up or comfort someone.

cork (kôrk) 1. Stopper for a bottle. 2. Put a stopper at the mouth of a bottle.

cor·ral (kə-răl′) Fenced-in place where animals can be kept.

crack·le (krăk′əl) Make short snapping noises.

crate (krāt) Wooden box in which things are shipped.

creek (krēk) Small stream of water.

crow (krō) Large black bird.

crow (krō) 1. Sound made by a male bird. 2. Brag; talk with too much pride.

crum·ple (krŭm′pəl) Fold up; wrinkle.

D

dan·der (dăn′dər) Temper; anger. — **get one's dander up.** *All right in everyday talk.* Become very angry.

dart (därt) 1. Small arrow usually thrown by hand. 2. Move suddenly and quickly.

de·clare (dĭ-klâr′) Say.

deed (dēd) 1. Something done. 2. Written agreement to buy or sell something.

de·spair (dĭ-spâr′) 1. Loss of all hope. 2. Give up; lose hope.

dis·grace (dĭs-grās′) Shame; dishonor. — **in disgrace.** In trouble because of having misbehaved.

E

earth·quake (ûrth′kwāk) Shaking of the earth caused by movements underneath the ground.

e·nor·mous (ĕ-nôr′məs) Very large.

e·vap·o·rate (ĭ-văp′ə-rāt) 1. Disappear slowly: *His cheerfulness evaporated as one thing after another went wrong.* 2. Change into tiny drops of water that are carried off into the air: *The sun's heat soon evaporated the water in the puddle.*

ex·pen·sive (ĕk-spĕn′sĭv) High-priced.

ă pat / ā pay / âr care / ä father / ĕ pet / ē be / ĭ pit / ī pie / îr fierce / ŏ pot / ō toe / ô paw, for / oi noise / ou out / o͝o took / o͞o boot / th thin / *th* this / ŭ cut / ûr turn / yo͞o use / ə about / zh pleasure

F

fade (fād) 1. Lose brightness of color. 2. Slowly disappear.

faith·ful (fāth′fəl) Loyal; trustworthy; true.

fan·ta·sy (făn′tə-sē) Fanciful story that could not really happen.

feat (fēt) Something done in spite of its being dangerous or hard to do.

fe·ver (fē′vər) 1. Higher than normal body temperature. 2. Strong feeling of eagerness or excitement.

fib (fĭb) Statement or story that is not true.

fil·ly (fĭl′ē) Young female horse.

flame (flām) Blaze from a fire.

force (fôrs) 1. Strength; power. 2. The police. 3. Push open: *The firemen will force the locked door.* 4. Make someone do something against his will.

fran·tic (frăn′tĭk) Wildly excited; worried; desperate.

fund (fŭnd) 1. Money saved for a special purpose. 2. Cash on hand.

G

gap (găp) Opening or empty space.

gaze (gāz) 1. Look for a long time. 2. Steady, staring look.

gen·er·ous (jĕn′ər-əs) Willing to give or share.

glide (glīd) Move around smoothly and easily, as on skates.

gov·ern·ment (gŭv′ərn-mənt) 1. Way or system by which a country, state, or city is ruled. 2. People who rule a country, state, or city.

grat·ing (grā′tĭng) Unpleasant to hear.

grat·ing (grā′tĭng) Covering for a hole in a street or sidewalk. The covering is usually made of crossed bars of metal.

graze (grāz) Eat grass.

grease·wood (grēs′woŏd) Bush found in the western part of the United States.

grip (grĭp) Tight hold.

grum·ble (grŭm′bəl) Complain; mutter in a complaining manner.

guard (gärd)   1. Watch over to keep from harm.   2. One who keeps watch.   3. Act of watching over.

H

hack (hăk)   Chop or cut away.

har·ness (här′nĭs)   Set of straps and buckles made to hitch to animals.

harvest (här′vĭst)   Season when a crop is ready to be picked.

hedge (hĕj)   1. Not answer a question directly and plainly.   2. Row of bushes or other plants used to form a fence.

he·ro (hîr′ō)   1. Person known for his bravery.   2. Famous person who is looked up to.

hes·i·tant (hĕz′ə-tənt)   1. Slow to decide to do something.   2. Shy; unsure; uncertain.

hes·i·tate (hĕz′ə-tāt)   1. Pause.   2. Be slow to decide or uncertain.

hous·ing proj·ect   (hou′zĭng prŏj′ĕkt)   Large apartment house or group of apartment houses in a city: *A housing project is sometimes built with money from the government.*

hutch (hŭch)   Box or pen for small animals such as rabbits.

I

in·i·tial (ĭ-nĭsh′əl)   First letter of a person's name.

in·tro·duce (ĭn-trə-dōōs′)   1. Present or show for the first time.   2. Bring together people who have never met before.

in·vent (ĭn-vĕnt′)   1. Make up.   2. Do or make something for the first time.

isle (īl)   Small island.

K

ka·bob (kə-bŏb′)   Meat and vegetables cooked on long pins called skewers.

ketch·up (kĕch′əp)   Also **catsup.** Thick, spicy tomato sauce used on many foods such as hamburgers.

ă pat / ā pay / âr care / ä father / ĕ pet / ē be / ĭ pit / ī pie / îr fierce / ŏ pot / ō toe / ô paw, for / oi noise / ou out / ŏŏ took / ōō boot / th thin / *th* this / ŭ cut / ûr turn / yōō use / ə about / zh pleasure

L

la·bel (lā′bəl) Piece of paper on a package or bottle telling something about its contents.

lan·tern (lăn′tərn) Box with glass or paper sides to shelter a light from wind and rain.

lev·el (lĕv′əl) 1. On an even line. 2. Flat. 3. Story of a building: *the top level of the house.* 4. Tool used to tell if something is flat: *Levels are often used by carpenters in building houses.*

lin·ger (lĭng′gər) Be slow to leave.

liq·uid (lĭk′wĭd) Something that flows and can be easily poured, such as milk or water.

M

main (mān) Largest or most important: *The street running through the center of a town is often called "Main Street."*

man·age (măn′ĭj) 1. Be able to do something. 2. Direct or operate: *to manage a store.* 3. Get along.

mane (mān) Long hair on the back of a horse's neck.

marsh (märsh) Soft, very wet land.

mea·sles (mē′zəlz) Disease, most commonly caught by children, in which the skin breaks out with red spots.

men·tal (mĕn′təl) Having to do with the mind: *A crossword puzzle is a good mental exercise.*

me·sa (mā′sə) Hill with steep sides and a flat top.

mis·er·a·ble (mĭz′ər-ə-bəl) Very unhappy or uncomfortable.

mur·mur (mûr′mər) 1. Speak softly in a way not easily heard. 2. Low series of muttering sounds.

mut·ter (mŭt′ər) 1. Speak in a low voice, often complaining to oneself. 2. Speech that is low and unclear.

N

neigh (nā) Sound made by a horse.

nib·ble (nĭb′əl) In fishing, a feeling on the line of a slight tug as a fish bites at the bait.

nor·mal (nôr′məl) 1. Usual. 2. Natural. 3. As it should be.

O

oak (ōk) Very large, leafy tree on which acorns grow.

ob·ject (ŏb′jĭkt) 1. Anything that can be seen or touched. 2. Purpose; aim.

ob·ject (əb-jĕkt′) Make a statement against something; complain; protest.

odd (ŏd) 1. Opposite of "even": *2 and 4 are even numbers; 3 and 5 are odd numbers.* 2. Strange; unusual.

P

pal·o·mi·no (păl-ə-mē′nō) Light tan or golden horse with a white mane and tail.

per·fect (pûr′fĭkt) 1. Whole; complete. 2. Having no faults.

per·fect (pər-fĕkt′) Improve; make whole; make perfect.

phase (fāz) 1. Passing manner of behaving that will not last long. 2. One of the ways a heavenly body looks to us: *The quarter moon is one phase of the moon.*

pier (pîr) Platform built from the shore to a point out in water where boats can be tied up.

plaque (plăk) Flat plate, sometimes used as a sign on a monument or statue.

plas·ter (plăs′tər) Mixture that looks like paste and hardens when dry: *Plaster casts are often put on broken arms or legs while they heal.*

pop·u·lar (pŏp′yə-lər) Well-liked by many people.

pos·sess (pə-zĕs′) Own; have.

prof·it (prŏf′ĭt) Money made on a business after expenses have been paid.

prog·ress (prŏg′rĕs) 1. Improvement. 2. Movement toward getting something done.

pro·gress (prə-grĕs′) 1. Move forward. 2. Move toward something better.

proj·ect (prŏj′ĕkt) Plan for making something or doing a piece of work. See also **housing project**.

ă pat / ā pay / âr care / ä father / ĕ pet / ē be / ĭ pit / ī pie / îr fierce / ŏ pot / ō toe / ô paw, for / oi noise / ou out / o͝o took / o͞o boot / th thin / *th* this / ŭ cut / ûr turn / yo͞o use / ə about / zh pleasure

prompt (prŏmpt) 1. Ready and quick to act. 2. On time. 3. Remind a person of words he has forgotten. 4. Done at once.

prop·er·ty (prŏp′ər-tē) Anything that is owned; used especially when talking about land that is owned.

pub·lic (pŭb′lĭk) Open to all people.

Q

quar·ter (kwôr′tər) 1. One-fourth; one of 4 equal parts. 2. Twenty-five cents.

quay (kē) Bank of a body of water so built that ships can load and unload cargo directly from and onto it.

queue (kyōō) 1. Line of people waiting for something. 2. Long pigtail.

R

rack·et (răk′ĭt) Light bat with network of crossed strings used in playing tennis and like games.

rack·et (răk′ĭt) Uproar; lot of noise.

ranch (rănch) Large farm where cows, horses, or other animals are raised.

range (rānj) Open land where cattle graze.

rear (rîr) Stand up on the hind legs.

rec·ord (rĕk′ərd) 1. Round, flat object that makes music or other sounds when used on a phonograph. 2. Written report of facts for others to read. 3. Best or greatest ever known: *His high jump set a world's record.*

re·cord (rĭ-kôrd′) 1. Sing, speak, or make music for the making of a phonograph record. 2. Write facts or thoughts to be kept for later use.

re·lief (rĭ-lēf′) 1. Gladness that a problem has been solved. 2. Freedom from worry or pain. 3. Sent in to take another's place: *a relief baseball pitcher.*

re·spon·si·ble (rĭ-spŏn′sə-bəl) Trustworthy; dependable; answerable for the safety and well-being of someone or something.

rogue (rōg) 1. Dishonest person. 2. One who is often up to some mischief.

root (rōōt) Underground part of a plant.

S

scamp (skămp) 1. Youngster who likes to play jokes and tricks. 2. Rogue; dishonest person.

scraw·ny (skrô'nē) Very skinny.

sec·tion (sĕk'shən) One of several parts of a building or area.

sen·sa·tion·al (sĕn-sā'shən-əl) 1. Outstanding; very good. 2. Very exciting.

serv·ice (sûr'vĭs) Work done for others as a business or as part of the government: *the mail service.*

se·vere (sə-vîr') 1. Stern or harsh: *She got a severe scolding.* 2. Causing great pain.

shriek (shrēk) Make a loud scream or cry of fear.

shrink (shrĭngk) Become smaller.

shud·der (shŭd'ər) Tremble with fear, dread, or cold.

sift (sĭft) 1. Pass through an object with small holes. 2. Push something through such an object: *sift flour.*

sig·nal (sĭg'nəl) Sign that gives commands or information.

skew·er (skyoo'ər) Long pin stuck through meat and vegetables to keep them in shape while they are being cooked.

slope (slōp) Piece of land that slants upward or downward.

snort (snôrt) Sound made by a horse when it breathes out noisily.

soar (sôr) Fly high into the air without seeming to have to work hard.

so·ber (sō'bər) Serious; calm; not joking.

spat·ter (spăt'ər) Splash of something in many drops: *We could hear the spatter of rain.*

spite (spīt) 1. Meanness; a wish to hurt another. 2. Be mean; hurt someone else: *He said unkind things to spite his friend.* **— in spite of.** Even though; even with: *He worked all day in spite of his bad cold.*

squash (skwŏsh) 1. Kind of vegetable that grows on vines. See also **banana squash.**

squash (skwŏsh) Squeeze; crush.

ă pat / ā pay / âr care / ä father / ĕ pet / ē be / ĭ pit / ī pie / îr fierce / ŏ pot / ō toe / ô paw, for / oi noise / ou out / oo took / oo boot / th thin / *th* this / ŭ cut / ûr turn / yoo use / ə about / zh pleasure

squint (skwĭnt) Look with eyes partly closed: *The bright sunlight made Joe squint when he first walked outside.*

stalk (stôk) Stem of a plant. The word is often used in compound words like *beanstalk.*

stalk (stôk) Walk quietly so as to sneak up on something or someone.

stall (stôl) Part of a barn where a horse is kept.

startle (stär′təl) Surprise suddenly and without warning.

state (stāt) 1. Place with its own government that may also come under the rule of a larger central government. 2. Say. 3. The way something or someone is: *Jack was in a worried state before the test.*

stock (stŏk) Farm animals such as horses, cattle, sheep, pigs, and goats.

stout (stout) 1. Strong and solid. 2. Fat. 3. Brave: *stout-hearted men.*

stow (stō) 1. Put away. 2. Arrange in place.

stuff (stŭf) 1. Fill with something: *to stuff a turkey with* dressing. 2. Pack too full. 3. Eat too much. 4. Anything at all when one does not know exactly what it is: *What is that green stuff all over the tree trunk?*

stun (stŭn) Make someone unable to speak or act naturally, usually by means of a blow, a loud noise, or something that is said.

stunt (stŭnt) Trick or feat that shows unusual strength, skill, or daring. **—pull a stunt.** Do such a trick.

suc·cess (sək-sĕs′) The getting of what one has wanted.

suede (swād) Kind of leather often used to make gloves, jackets, and other clothing.

swell (swĕl) 1. Get bigger. 2. Cause to grow bigger. 3. *All right in everyday talk.* Very nice; very likable.

sword (sôrd) Weapon with a long blade and sharp edge or edges.

T

tan (tăn) 1. Yellowish-brown color. 2. Darken the skin by being out in the sun.

tan·gle (tăng′gəl) 1. Twist around. 2. Mix in a disorderly way. 3. Disorderly mixture.

tel·e·scope (tĕl′ə-skōp) 1. Object one can look through to see stars, planets, and satellites more closely. 2. Slide together so that one part folds into another.

tel·e·vise (tĕl′ə-vīz) Send or receive by TV.

tem·ple (tĕm′pəl) Building used as a place of worship.

ter·ri·fy (tĕr′ə-fī) Cause great fear.

ther·mom·e·ter (thər-mŏm′ə-tər) Object used for measuring the temperature of the air, of a liquid, or of a person's body.

thrust (thrŭst) 1. Push quickly. 2. Sudden push.

thud (thŭd) Dull sound such as that made by something heavy hitting the ground or floor.

tim·id (tĭm′ĭd) Shy; a little afraid to do something.

toad·stool (tōd′stool) Small, umbrella-shaped plant that often grows in wet ground.

tone (tōn) 1. Way of speaking. 2. Color. 3. Musical sound.

torch (tôrch) Burning stick usually carried in the hand.

torment (tôr-mĕnt′) 1. Tease and upset in a mean way. 2. Cause great pain.

tow·er (tou′ər) Rise to great height.

trace (trās) Anything left behind: *He disappeared without a trace.*

trans·par·ent (trăns-pâr′ənt) Easily seen through: *Window glass is transparent.*

trot (trŏt) Easygoing running movement slightly faster than a walk.

trunk (trŭngk) 1. Part of a car used for stowing such things as suitcases or spare tires. 2. Elephant's long nose. 3. Main part of a tree. 4. Large packing box.

ă pat / ā pay / âr care / ä father / ĕ pet / ē be / ĭ pit / ī pie / îr fierce / ŏ pot / ō toe / ô paw, for / oi noise / ou out / oo took / oo boot / th thin / *th* this / ŭ cut / ûr turn / yoo use / ə about / zh pleasure

U

urge (ûrj) 1. Very strong wish to do something. 2. Beg or ask forcefully.

V

val·u·a·ble (văl′yoo͞-ə-bəl) Highly useful; worth a great deal.

vexed (věkst) Upset; troubled; angry.

W

whim·per (hwĭm′pər) 1. Low, broken, crying sound. 2. Cry softly.

wield (wēld) Hold and use as a tool.

Y

yacht (yät) Boat used mainly for fun.

Artist Credits

Donald Leake *(Cover, title page, and magazine covers, pages 7, 113, 209)*

Illustrations: Marc Brown *(pages 110–111, 282–284, 285);* Kevin Callahan *(pages 96–109);* John Dawson *(page 154);* Robert DeCoste *(pages 178–181);* Blair Drawson *(pages 52–60);* Shan Ellentuck *(pages 116–130);* Ed Emberley *(pages 80–93);* John Freas *(pages 138, 139–141);* Ethel Gold *(pages 236–252);* John Ham *(pages 48–51, 75–78, 115, 132–137, 191–194, 228–233, 286–291);* Gordon Kibbee *(pages 292–305);* Hilary Knight *(pages 211–227);* Tad Krumeich *(page 190);* Elaine Livermore *(page 142);* Kenneth Longtemps *(143–153);* Ikki Matsumoto *(pages 206–207);* David McPhail *(pages 36, 234–235);* Bill Morrison *(pages 254–281);* Jan Palmer *(page 131);* Tom Quinn *(pages 155–174);* Marty Richardson *(pages 61, 95);* Eleonore Schmid *(pages 182–189);* Charles Schulz *(page 74);* Cyndy Szekeres-Prozzo *(pages 62–73);* Kyuzo Tsugami *(pages 196–205);* Bernard Waber *(pages 37–47);* Cecile Webster *(pages 9–34).*

Photographs: Erik Anderson *(pages 35 top, 253);* David Kelley *(page 94);* Anna Kaufman Moon *(pages 79, 195);* Tanner Ottley *(page 35 bottom);* The Seeing Eye, Inc., Morristown, N. J. *(pages 175–177)*